Aphorisms
FROM LATHAM

PETER MERE LATHAM

Aphorisms

FROM LATHAM

COLLECTED AND EDITED BY

William B. Bean, M.D.

Head of the Department of Internal Medicine
College of Medicine, State University of Iowa

The Prairie Press
IOWA CITY

ACKNOWLEDGMENTS

I should like to thank Dr. Richard H. Young, Dean of the Northwestern University Medical School for letting me have a copy of Latham's photograph to use as a frontispiece and Dr. John L. Thornton, the Librarian of the Medical College Library of St. Bartholomew's Hospital, London, who has been very helpful in getting another photograph for me which, unfortunately, was not suitable for reproduction.

I should like to acknowledge my great indebtedness to several secretaries, Mrs. Charlotte Fell, Mrs. Marilyn Sanner, Mrs. Patsy French and Mrs. Ellen Goldberg who worked on this manuscript and related matters.

To physicians and scholars
who savor elegance in style and excellence in character,
this revival of the words and thoughts of one
of medicine's noblemen is dedicated.

Contents

Aphorisms

FROM LATHAM

Introduction

Time, with its slow desiccations, has covered our memory of most men with a heavy pall of forgetfulness. A classic victim of the all-pervading poppy of oblivion is Peter Mere Latham whose splendid traits as a physician and teacher are entombed in his clinical lectures and textbooks. What undergraduate or indeed what clinician knows of him? No one knows him. Latham's interest focused on the patient. How best to teach young students and practitioners about the sick person and so disclose the arts as well as the science of medicine? His explicit purpose was to provide in writing a bedside companion for eager young men who wished to learn to be good doctors. He presented facts clearly and lucidly. He did not bedevil the student with fine-spun theories or the host of authoritarian opinions quoted at such interminable length in the nosologies of his day. Lucid style and engaging personality sparkle in his writings. He treats even the most abstruse subject matter directly and simply, making it seem easy. Latham's courtly and benign view of his contemporaries and predecessors kept him from insulting anyone. His searching critiques grew out of his extensive bedside experience. He was wise enough at the age of twenty-six, on his appointment as physician to the Middlesex Hospital, to "shut up his books and try to judge for himself."

Osler's comment on Latham's character aroused my curiosity when I read it more than twenty-five years ago. It prompted me to order Latham's *Lectures on Subjects Connected with Clinical Medicine* from a catalogue of old medical books. This

I read and reread during certain "spare hours" of some seasons in the Army from 1942 to 1946. Here indeed was a book which was a proper companion, growing richer and mellower with repeated study. I have long been in the habit of marking passages which please me so that I can find them at a glance and reread them. This is why it is dangerous for me to read books which do not belong to me. I read a book as I converse, reacting agreeing, fighting, arguing, or expressing as well as feeling delight. I write, underline, dog-ear and otherwise leave the spoor of an engaged reader. After some years this little book had nearly as many lines underscored as not, many notes, some question marks and a lot of Amens!

The capacity to frame useful matter in elegant manner was a characteristic of Latham's writing. I have collected his published books and gathered what I could from his numerous casual contributions to the journals and periodicals of his time. I have lent, lost and later had returned several copies of Latham's books, each underlined separately and independently of any earlier reading. To my surprise there *is* consistency in my selections. Much of the material was underlined identically in different editions. There were, of course, some variations for his writing was so compact, so well polished and so self-contained that it had the quality of aphorism and the attribute of epitome. Thus began my collection of Latham's aphorisms now presented with the hope that they may lead others to seek out his original works and feel at first hand the charm, the radiance, the kindness and the warm goodness of this master teacher and delightful man.

After I had gathered these aphorisms I was pleased to find an elder companion in praise of Latham. Herrick, in his charming book "A Short History of Cardiology", remarks that "Latham's lectures abound in epigrams that must have helped fix the attention of his hearers and readers upon his statements that were so often wise and philosophic." Herrick quoted some of the passages which I had included. This was a sufficient stimulus to put the collection in order and explain why I had done it.

The question has often been asked, What makes an epigrammatist? What qualities produce the "burrs that stick in the memory?" Fulton has suggested two main elements in the makeup of the master of epigram. "He must be a philosopher with a deep interest in and understanding of humankind and he must have the gift of stating simple truths in terse, crisp language." To this combination I hasten to add merely that what is so casually taken to be the gift for clear, deft writing is not a present from the gods or from carefully selected forebears so much as the by-product of hard work, long practice and concentration in training. To these must be added an ear for language.

Can we find any clue why Latham "could wrap up wisdom in a witticism," as he said about someone else? Sir Thomas Watson's memorial essay, "Biographical Note on Latham," published in the St. Bartholomew's Hospital Reports, gives some hints by way of answer but leaves undecided the assignment of credit to heredity or environment if indeed we can separate these two aspects of life. Those who lay stress on early impressions and influence will have a hard time reconciling Latham's extreme idleness as a schoolboy, (remember John Hunter, that naturalist incorrigibly illiterate as an adolescent). Latham hated Latin and Greek. Later he mastered them. Some unknown teacher caught his fancy and stirred his desire for excellence, because in 1809, at the age of twenty, he won the undergraduate's prize for Latin verse at Oxford. This skill in Latin composition is manifest in his later Harveian Oration which scholars used to revere as the last such essay praiseworthy for its polished Latin.

Anyone interested in excellence of style will see that Latham owed much to his training in Latin for the stately and elegant writing, always clear, strong and precise. But he rose above it. He escaped formal style to build his own. He abounds in those sudden quaint turns and stage whispers which reveal the epigram as though one were brushing aside the curtains to see a chiseled inscription. Today a classical education has all but van-

13

ished. Now that current medical writing calls to mind long and monotonous marches through a wasteland, educators might ponder the lesson of discipline in the mastery of another language, almost any language. Just as teaching a subject immediately discloses to us unrecognized flaws in our own knowledge, so translating into a foreign language reveals our ignorance and misconceptions about our native tongue.

No less worthy of notice than his preprofessional education was Latham's training in medicine. He studied at St. Bartholomew's Hospital before the clinical clerkship had become established. Senior students were attached to the attending physicians as apprentices, watching the practice and supervising such care as patients got. Latham was not content to confine his own studies to being supervised by Dr. Haworth at St. Bartholomew's. In his lust to learn he observed the practice of Dr. Bateman at the Carey Street Dispensary. There he had the good fortune to meet Richard Bright who became a lifelong friend. In times of stress, notably during the fearfully cold winter of 1814 when the misery and disease among the poorer classes in London were appalling, the dispensary physicians could not themselves manage all the patients. Great clinical responsibility was turned over to Bright, Latham and other students. There they became skilled, and, devoted to medical learning and to sick patients, they became medical scholars.

Most noteworthy in Latham's continuing as a medical student after becoming a physician was his discernment in the matter of reading books and observing patients and disease. He was profoundly influenced by his sense of duty and responsibility. He began to expose his enormous capacity for work, his conscientious care and devotion to patients and his ability to grow in medical wisdom as well as in years. As a young bachelor it was his custom to dine at Harley Street with his father, who was a distinguished physician too. On the way home he would stop at St. Bartholomew's Hospital to observe his patients. His thoughtful and conscientious attention to their comfort and his kindness in those often neglected and seemingly trivial matters

14

which mean so much to the sick were rewarded by the opportunity to study patients at casual moments when disease may be taken off guard. He read the quiet clues by which illness often discloses its nature in an aside not recognized by the untutored and not seen by the absent. He transmuted these parentheses of illness into the exclamation marks of clinical skill.

But this care was not miscellaneous and random. He gathered information, studied it carefully and crystallized the salient features. From them he was able to make broad and pertinent generalizations. He meditated. His own self-criticism, unsung heroism, is revealed in a remarkable study he did at St. Bartholomew's Hospital. For ten years he collected, arranged and digested material for a comprehensive treatise on Continued Fevers. His clinical clerks, chosen with care, had kept every last detail in his immaculate case books. These he systematically analyzed and assimilated. His method was to bleed one in every four of his fever patients and to compare their mortality with that of the remainder of the group, who had all been leeched. The disease first under study seems to have been mostly typhoid fever. Those who died had ulcerated bowels. But the entire program of study was upset by the subtle intercurrence and intermingling of typhus fever with its mottled eruptions of the skin, petechiae, and its much higher mortality rate. Typhus and typhoid fever had not yet been clearly separated when he was at work. This confusion which he sensed but did not clearly understand was so disturbing that he never let his intended book see the light of day. He felt that he could not judge his own data. These golden years of effort, the whole vast enterprise seemed wasted. But their reward was the clinical wisdom which sparkles in the works he did publish.

It is very easy for us today to look back with superiority and scorn on the labors of our medical ancestors. We must all admire the stern integrity which made Latham withhold these diligently gathered fruits of ten years of enormous labor in clinical observation, a lesson which every investigator must take to heart. Latham had a rigorous sense of duty, of the responsibility

15

of the physician, and particularly of the responsibility of the teacher or writer of things medical. Today many aspects of medical thought play up the individual person, the resolution of personal troubles and conflicts without concern for the near or far effects on others. It is refreshing to see such vigorous and consistent self-monitoring as we find in Latham. Added to his abiding and imperative sense of duty he had the temper of mind which loved order, method and regularity. This shines through his writings. Precision and a fastidious sense of language reveal the mature self-critic. His statements did not grow, fungus-like out of any mental chaos. They were the result of careful focus on clarity of expression and accuracy of style. They convey his meaning unambiguously. Lest anyone think that an aim for excellence, a high sense of duty and perfectionism have to be associated with asperities of personality, he must look at Watson's delightful essay in which Latham's character and life are depicted by a sincere, enthusiastic but perceptive friend. Latham himself can be epitomized by words he used about his own beloved brother, John as — "An example of that peculiarly English character, the unobtrusive but accomplished high-minded Christian gentleman". Thus he is eminently worthy to join that great company of physicians who "have influenced the profession less by their special work than by exemplifying those graces of life and refinements of heart which make character."

Now we turn to the aphorisms.

REFERENCES

Sir William Osler: Aphorisms from his Bedside Teachings and his Writings, Bean, R. Bennett and Bean, William Bennett, First Edition. Henry Schuman, New York, 1950.

Sir William Osler: Aphorisms from his Bedside Teachings and his Writings, Bean, R. Bennett and Bean, William Bennett, Second Printing. Charles C. Thomas Publisher, Springfield, Illinois, 1961.

Herrick, J. B., A Short History of Cardiology. Charles C. Thomas, Springfield, Illinois, 1942.

Watson, T., In Memoriam. The Collected Works of Dr. P. M. Latham, Ed. Robert Martin, The New Sydenham Society, London, 1876.

Williamson, R. T., English Physicians of the Past. Biography of John Latham, p. 76, Andrew Reid and Company Ltd., Newcastle-Upon-Tyne, England, 1923.

Williamson, R. T., English Physicians of the Past. Biography of Peter Mere Latham, p. 80, Andrew Reid and Company Ltd., Newcastle-Upon-Tyne, England, 1923.

Greenwood, Major, The Medical Dictator, Williams and Norgate, Ltd., London, 1936.

17

Motto

"MY BUSINESS is to attend the sick,
and to aid the studies of those who
seek the knowledge of disease at the
bed-side of the patient."

LATHAM

Aphorisms
FROM LATHAM

THE ARTS OF MEDICINE

The powers of art must be brought to overrule the operations of nature by force. To know these powers and how to wield them to such a purpose is an affair beyond all trick and all skill of practicing upon the fancies of mankind. It can only proceed from a faithful and candid search after truth by each of us for himself according to his opportunities, and for a ready communication of what we believe to be the truth by all of us among one another, and from a comparison of their experiences and conclusions among the best minds.

Men bear no mark that I know of denoting their great or their small susceptibility to mercury.

I am persuaded that when the physician is called upon to perform great things, even to arrest destructive disease, and to save life, his skill in wielding the implements of his art rests mainly upon the right understanding of simple and single indications, and of the remedies which have power to fulfil them.

This is the skill which cures diseases and saves lives. And no man ever had it, who did not obtain it from his own self-teaching amid the emergencies of actual practice.

19

The nervous system may become wild with suffering, and then it is not to be soothed and coaxed into quietude, but to be subdued.

I can tell you how to manage a disease, but not how to manage a case. One man may learn the principles of an art from another's discourse; but he must learn its practice, not from hearing him talk about it, but from seeing him in the act of exercising the art itself.

Medicine is a strange mixture of speculation and action. We have to cultivate a science and to exercise an art. The calls of science are upon our leisure and our choice; the calls of practice are of daily emergence and necessity.

Of what endless and still increasing necessity is this business of clinical observation to the improvement of our art! All that has been found out by those who have gone before us does not leave less, but more to be sought after by ourselves.

The artist, whatever may be the material he uses, for his projected work, whether wood or stone, takes care to have the most perfectly sound specimen of it he can get; knowing that, otherwise, the work itself is likely enough to turn out a failure, and be neither so good nor so durable as his ambition might hope. And we physicians, when we want Inflammation for a study of Fever, would like to choose the subjects whom it should befall, and have them of the soundest material. But we must take cases as they come. We are practitioners by necessity; we are pathologists by choice or by chance. It is well then we *can* be both, but the first we *must* be.

If all life were the life of distinct organs and nothing more, and if health and disease were nothing more than what distinct organs could work out for themselves through their own functions singly and independently; and if, moreover, nature had

20

supplied the means by which all organs and their functions could be reached, and man had learnt the skill of using such means with perfect safety and success; then, indeed, would medicine be a certain art.

When we speak most modestly of medicine, we call it nothing more than a conjectural art. But this conjectural art so closely borders upon the neighborhood of the sciences, and draws so much from their principles and discoveries, that we may be pardoned for sometimes calling it, and even believing it to be, itself a science.

There are peculiar causes which will ever prevent medicine from arriving at the certainty of purely physical science.

PATIENT AND PHYSICIAN

There are always two parties of the management of the disease — the physician and the patient.

The first aim of the physician in such cases should always be to make the patient clearly to understand what his state is, and to see the reasonableness of the advice that is given him. For his treatment, though it may proceed upon our suggestion, must be entirely carried on by himself. It must engage every hour of his life, and be allowed to interfere with all his habits, and conduct, and objects. A man, therefore, had need be well persuaded, that what we require him to do is right, when the doing it calls for so large an amount of self-sacrifice.

Is it possible to feel an interest in all this? Ay, indeed it is; a greater, far greater interest than ever painter or sculptor took in the form and beauties of its health . . . Whence comes this interest? At first, perhaps, it seldom comes naturally: a mere sense of duty must engender it; and still, for a while, a mere sense of duty must keep it alive. Presently the quick, curious, restless spirit of science enlivens it; and then it becomes an excitement and a pleasure, and then the deliberate choice of the mind . . . When the interest of attending the sick has reached this point, there arises from it, or has already arisen, a ready discernment of diseases, with a skill in the use of remedies. And the skill may exalt the interest, and the interest may improve the skill, until, in process of time, experience forms the consummate practitioner . . . But does the interest of attending the sick necessarily stop here? The question may seem strange. If it has led to the readiest discernment and the highest skill, and formed the consummate practitioner, why need it go further? . . . But what if humanity shall warm it? Then this interest, this excitement, this intellectual pleasure, is exalted into a principle, and invested with a moral motive, and passes into the heart. What if it be carried still further? What if religion should animate it? Why, then, happy indeed is that man whose mind, whose moral nature, and whose spiritual being, are all harmoniously engaged in the daily business of his life; with whom the same act has become his own happiness, a dispensation of mercy to his fellow-creatures and a worship of God.

The practice of physic is jostled by quacks on the one side, and by science on the other.

In the daily practice of medicine, things in themselves mean and of no account, do often, by their place and by their relations, gain a just preponderance over things more prominent and striking, and have the largest share in guiding our decision upon the most important questions.

The discerning public delights in nothing more than a change of physicians for the novelty of the thing. And for this, as for other novelties, it is apt to pay dear.

He consults an infinite number of medical men; and it is remarkable that he gets no comfort or satisfaction from those who understand his disease the best, and the greatest comfort and satisfaction from those who understand nothing about it. Those, who know what it is, out of kindness do not tell him the truth, and they cannot asseverate a falsehood stoutly enough to carry any weight with it.

A rare enough thing to meet with among physicians is this wisely expectant mind. It presumes a study and sound judgment of the sort and measure of evidence which the subject admits, and a decision habitually exercised upon it; not demanding more, but never content with less.

And to this end, among the many uncertainties of medicine, they have been always in quest of those few things belonging to it which are more sure and stable, and how and where in every case to lay hold of them, and to use them, and to make the most and the best of them.

Among the perils of disease we must not refuse to reckon the errors of physicians. Nor among the perils of disease must we refuse to reckon the interference of friends with its treatment.

Practical medicine is unlike all other things in the world.

Patients themselves are apt to press upon their medical attendant, symptoms (generally consisting of strange sensations) which are irrelevant to their present disease.

Besides, the patient himself, by an over anxious and over constant attention to what he feels, is liable to miscalculate the kind and quantity of his own sufferings, and thus to mislead you by exaggerating every little ache into an intolerable grievance . . . Again; the patient himself, by habitual disregard of what he feels, is liable to miscalculate in the opposite way. He either has

23

no pain, or he owns to none, where another would complain of a great deal; and thus he misleads you by extenuating a real grievance, or entirely passing it by. Neither of these can be safely trusted for a correct interpretation of their own sensations . . . Plain sensible men, who feel just what they ought to do, and tell just what they feel, are the most agreeable patients to attend.

Soft, delicate, nervous persons, who feel extravagantly, and still exaggerate what they feel, are very troublesome to deal with. You are not certain that they do not deceive both you and themselves; and such a perplexity is cast over their complaints, that you can neither understand them nor treat them properly.

There are also cases in which there are no indications prominent or clear enough to become the special scope of practice, and in which time and opportunity have been postponed or lost, so that medicine is never sure of its aim; or, if it should happen to take the right one, it could hardly expect to reach it. These we call *bad* cases. We dislike them, and flinch from them, and can only bring ourselves to treat them as a matter of duty.

Happily for mankind, there are, and always have been, physicians who have sought to practice their profession with as much exactness as its nature will allow.

Unquestionably, there is no better introduction to the practice of physic than the practice of surgery.

But Nature, in all her powers and operations, allows herself to be led, directed, and controlled. And to lead, direct, or control for purposes of good, this is the business of the physician.

To understand, then, tolerably well what is this limit of *practical* thought in medicine, and to walk circumspectly within it, is the secret of all the power we have of doing good.

It is a fine thing pretty soon in life to be employed and patronized by rich and great people; but it is not the surest way of making a good physician.

The best physicians have begun by being the physician of the poor.

It is sad to think how much of the practice of medicine is blindly engaged in a busy, noisy workshop of impossibilities.

On the other hand, among the rich and well-off classes of the community, the treatment of diseases is seldom as simple as it might be.

Doubtless, to the eye of the anatomist, the vascular system and the nervous system are things apart one from the other. But to the physiologist, the pathologist, and the practical physician, they are always mixed.

. . . the poor man's disease is the most severe, and calls the loudest for relief (for he does not succumb to trifles) . . .

. . . faith and knowledge lean largely upon each other in the practice of medicine.

Physicians, who have worthily achieved great reputation, become the refuge of the hopeless, and earn for themselves the misfortune of being expected to cure incurable diseases.

The physician gains strange insights into the weaknesses of poor human nature.

Yet as the ability to read does not make a man literary or learned, but only furnishes him the means, the indispensable means, however, of becoming so, so neither does the skill to decipher the auscultatory language of the heart make him all at

25

once a great pathologist or a good practitioner in respect of its diseases; but being constantly, soberly, and diligently applied, it furnishes him with much help towards surer knowledge and a better treatment of them. For auscultation is conversant with principles.

In actual practice, there is no such thing as choosing your own cases — you must take the good and the bad as they come.

If I undertake to instruct you out of my little book of experience, I hold it but honesty to read it straight through. There is no such thing as turning practical medicine into a well-told tale.

Physicians are in a manner often called upon to be wiser than they possibly can be. Disease or imperfection of a vital organ is a fearfully interesting thing to him who suffers it, and he presses to learn all that is known, and often much more than is known about it.

Physiology, pathology, and practice, often part company just where an intelligent looker-on would make sure of their becoming sociable and co-operative. The practice of medicine is a perpetual compromise between what we know and what we can do, between our knowledge and our power.

THE HISTORY OF MEDICINE

There was a practice of medicine long before there was any knowledge of disease. The griefs, pains, and necessities of man's body and mind did not call the less loudly for relief because they were not understood.

There is no room for disparaging our predecessors and glorifying ourselves, or for complimenting our present selves at the expense of our former selves.

The physicians of one time have been too prone to make a mock of what was deemed the sound practice of another. This is neither generous nor wise.

It ill beseems that impartiality which ought especially to characterize every enquiry after such truths as we are engaged in, to be bent upon depreciating the labours of the past age and exalting those of the present, or disparaging old methods of research and praising new ones. Pathology and practical medicine had assuredly made some respectable advances before we were born, and before physicians had found out all the uses of their ears, and of the stethoscope.

In the history of our profession we meet too often with things utterly worthless capriciously taken up, but sometimes with things really valuable capriciously laid aside.

If any man, a little accustomed to self-questioning, will call to mind what he was at first as a physician, and what by increase of knowledge and experience he afterwards became, he will find not infaithfully reflected in his own example the beginning and progress of the art itself.

A man need not have grown old in the practice of medicine to bear witness to its having undergone considerable changes . . .

Let a man use his own Experience as best he can for the present; but let him not, upon the strength of it, rebuke the Experience of all past times, and dictate to the Experience of all future; for, if he live long enough, nothing is more likely than that he may find himself fallen under his own reproof, and inconveniently confronted by his own maxims.

27

THE MEDICAL PROFESSION

What is this medical profession? It is the art how to treat, cure, and minister all possible relief to men, women, and children, when they have come to harm from disease, accident, or any other adversity.

The Profession of Medicine, in itself and in the things pertaining to it, is running over with knowledge. The studies proper, preparatory, and collateral to it, are enormous.

No sect, no party in politics, has reckoned many of our profession among its clamorous advocates: but wherever there has been any association of good men for laudable ends—wherever any great scheme of benevolence has been designed or perfected — medical men have been always found among their first, their most zealous, and useful promoters.

Medicine, as it begins to touch upon higher interests, even the interests of life and death, should feel itself in alliance with higher motives than any which can be thought to help and quicken its pursuit as mere science. For now it claims a sort of moral respect in the handling; it calls upon the conscience as well as the intellect, for more caution to avoid error, and more fearfulness of overstepping the truth.

It concerns physicians, above all men, that theirs should not be a barren knowledge, but that it should claim honour of mankind from a sense of the benefit which they receive from it.

I have a conservative jealousy of the rank due to my profession.

MEDICAL BOOKS

On my first entrance into my profession, and for some time afterwards, nothing was less intelligible to me than the writings of our great physicians.

Nosology, at the best, is but a sort of provisional pathology, telling us something, little, or nothing, as it may happen, about the nature of the disease, and the management thereof.

To tell the truth, most medical books have been a puzzle to me all my life long. Their descriptions of disease have been (to my thinking) needlessly complex and multifarious, mixing what is proper and constant, and first in order, with what is common, and variable, and consequential; both being real enough in themselves, but meaning different things.

Never read any book that bears internal marks of being addressed more to the public than to the profession. They are all bad, and many dishonest.

A bad book is generally a very easy book, having been composed by its author with no labour of mind whatever; whereas a good book, though it be not necessarily a hard one, yet, since it contains important facts, duly arranged, and reasoned upon with care, must require from the reader some portion of the same attention and study to comprehend and profit by it, as it required from the writer to compose it.

The writer of a good practical book on medicine, who tells the world something that it did not know before, something of large application in fortifying or restoring the health, strength, and comfort of man's body and mind; or who, if he tells nothing new, yet wisely sets in order what is already known, and gives it a better and more convenient adaptation to the same high purposes; such a writer, in all just estimate of things, is second, and second only, to the great expounders of moral and religious truth.

THE MEANING OF MEANING

Beware of language, for it is often a great cheat.

Medical men have never been remarkably exact about the meaning of the terms they employ.

It is not likely that in a profession like ours, which, itself and all belongings to it, suffers perpetual change, language should be constant to its meaning, and the same word continue for ever to express the same thing. Practical medicine must not be over-nice about the language it uses, or it will be brought to a stand-still altogether.

There are things which will not be defined, and Fever is one of them. Besides, when a word has passed into everyday use, it is too late to lay a logical trap for its meaning, and think to apprehend it by a definition.

Now Fever is a general term, and as such, carries with it the danger, as far as its meaning is concerned, of degenerating into a vague abstraction. And this danger is the greater, the more it is thought of and talked of, apart from the patients who suffer it.

All general terms in use among physicians had need to be jealously watched. Even strength and weakness, simple and innocent as they look, have by turns been the marring of us. The terms themselves cannot be dispensed with; and as long as they truly represent (as they always ought) an aggregate of things real, and verifiable in their details, they serve an useful purpose. But, failing this, they become pernicious abstractions.

30

Listen to the fellows in the street, how they bandy about some vulgar word from morning to night, giving and taking it in its now unmistakable sense, and little thinking of all the trouble some antiquarian philologer has had with it.

Things which all men know infallibly by their own perceptive experience, cannot be made plainer by words.

There are more realities in medicine than we have language to describe — realities known and acted upon and put to the proof every day. . .

At the bed-side we must be content to know less than we know anatomically, and to use terms which designate just what we know and no more.

They who profess to teach others out of their own experience, should be careful of using language which may imply more than that experience will justify.

Surely there is an evil in using language more precise than our knowledge. If this were the place, it would be easy to show that medicine has partaken especially of it. Its language has almost always outrun its knowledge. And the evil has been nothing less than this: our language, by ever persuading us that we are wiser than we are, has wedded us to many a capital error.

Almost all language is figurative, and so far may obscure as well as illustrate the subject which it is used to denote.

I have no fancy for disputing about names; but this I would remark, that you might just as well call an Aneurism a Haemorrhage, as a simple Dilatation of the air-cells, or the Rupture of the air-cells into each other, an Emphysema.

It is the great mystery of life itself which is at the bottom of all the mysterious language we are obliged to employ concerning it.

31

TRUTH —

How is it that in medicine Truth is measured out to us in fragments, and we are never put in trust of it *as a whole?*

Truth in all its kinds is most difficult to win; and truth in medicine is the most difficult of all.

It is no easy task to pick one's way from truth to truth through besetting errors.

Men do not go to work with the same good will to detect what they suspect will turn out an error, as to confirm what they hope to find a truth.

Let each fact be made to carry with it the full force of its own truth, and yet, in relation to other facts which are as true as itself, let it hold no higher value, place, or proportion, than nature has given it.

It takes as much time and trouble to pull down a falsehood as to build up a truth.

The next best thing to seeing, knowing, and getting well hold of the truth, is to clear away impediments that block up the road which leads to it.

Let me here, in as few words as possible, give you and myself a little caution against being unawares led to take various opinions and beliefs in medicine for settled truths, because the terms in current use among medical men would imply that they are so.

There are some truths in medicine which are based upon numbers and upon statistical calculations, and which thus carry with them the highest proof of their certainty. And there are others which are and only can be picked up piecemeal and by

32

accident; yet these may be equally truths in themselves, though they are not equally known to be so: they may be called chance-truths, lying out of the high road of philosophy; but Philosophy is not wise, if she does not step aside to gather them.

Next to knowing the truth itself, is to know the direction in which it lies. And this is the peculiar praise of a sound conjecture.

Such is the nature of medicine, that things which we have laid up in our minds as settled *truths* often require to be modified by our future experience, and come at last to be rated many degrees below the value at which we originally prized them.

It is an infirmity of men, finding a fragment of Truth, to take it for the whole Truth; or, intent upon what may well pass for Truth now and for a few years to come to account it the Truth which stands fast for ever and ever.

Nothing can be taken for *absolutely true* in practical medicine.

The truth which medicine is concerned with is a *truth of degrees;* the same, nevertheless, which the moral world is governed by. Wise men seek it and cultivate it, and make the best of it. In medicine there is small philosophy, and no use in making it seem less than it is.

If what can be apprehended by fragments but not completely, if what lasts safe and sure and trustworthy for times and seasons but not for ever, can be called Truth, this is the Truth, which is vouchsafed us to know and to use in the practice of medicine, and this only.

— AND ERROR

Unfortunately for us, the nature of medical causation is such, that it takes as much time and trouble to rectify an error as to establish a truth. Thus it may require the experience of one man's life to arrive at some plausible theory, and the counter-experience of another man's life to show that it is false.

When a disease is taken and treated for inflammation, and turns out to be no such thing, and taken and treated for curable, and turns out to be incurable, there is ignorance no doubt on our part, or there is mistake, and some may think there is blame. But it is such ignorance as must be, such mistake as cannot be helped, such blame as the best and wisest of us all have no power of escaping. From the nature of things it cannot be otherwise.

In medicine (what men are scarcely aware of until they become severely practical), it requires as much labour and time fairly to lay hold of an error, and uproot it, and have done with it, as to learn and settle a truth, and abide by it.

In this mode of proceeding our knowledge may be *incomplete,* but it is never erroneous. The mind advances from fact to fact, resting on one as the stepping-stone to another, and feeling safe in the possession of the truth, although it may not be *all the truth* that is capable of being ascertained.

It is well to be aware of so natural a bias towards error, and carefully to guard against it.

Laennec, in working out his proofs in detail, admitted some capital *errors,* which had well nigh made shipwreck of the whole discovery for any useful or practical purpose.

Amid many possibilities of error, it would be strange indeed to be always in the right.

THOUGHT —

It is safer to appeal to men's perceptions than to their logic.

All strenuous and earnest men, let their habitual work be what it may, if it have but a serious purpose, carry home with them plenty of matter for thought springing out of that work every day of their lives. It is eminently the case with physicians.

From things of easy and familiar use they gather intimation of truths which lie too deep for common observation. Thus, besides turning what can be turned to the best practical account according to the present duty and necessity, they put by facts and (it may be) thoughts for further inquiry and experiment, and hope thereby to gain new knowledge, or new adaptations of knowledge, and so render that which they have in exercise more sure and trustworthy.

Time and diligence, and constant intercourse with the sick, if you have but *an impartial and honest* mind, will enable you to lay up a large and useful store of genuine facts, and to draw from it as the treasury of your future knowledge. I say an *impartial* and an *honest* mind, because it is remarkable how apt some little favourite theory is to get early possession of the student's imagination, rendering him dishonest (perhaps unconsciously) in the simple reception of facts. It is like some little favourite sin in our moral nature, which taints the character of the whole man.

A premature desire to generalize, an eagerness to arrive at conclusions, and a readiness to rest in them, are very common infirmities, and they offer very serious hindrances to the right acquisition of facts.

Beware of rejecting facts of which you do not, perhaps, comprehend the import, and because you do not comprehend . . .

Bear in mind, then, that abstractions are *not facts;* and next bear in mind that *opinions* are not facts.

Follow great thinkers into their studies. In every age there are a few who are inwardly prompted to give a life's labour, that they "may, perhaps, leave something so written to aftertimes as they shall not willingly let it die."

Men's watches agree better together than their perceptions. Looking to our several watches, we have an index as nearly uniform as possible, and so we are always of one mind about the number of the pulse and its rhythm. Consulting our several perceptions, we use a variable index; and no wonder that about the *qualities* of the pulse we are apt to differ. Yet, after all, practical men are found to agree pretty well about the quality of the pulse in particular instances.

It is well to know the possible fallacy of our own thinking, and so to guard against it.

— AND SPECULATION

There are subjects upon which the most sober and practical minds cannot help speculating a little beyond what they know.

It is possible to speculate too curiously upon morbid sensations; to speculate even so far as to deceive ourselves respecting them.

It is a poor and profitless task to be guessing and speculating about mere matters of accident and uncertainty. It is the same thing as if a man, after he had read a book fairly through and mastered it, should think himself bound to count how many lines there were in each page, and how many words in each line.

Then comes the temptation common to all minds that are speculative (and what mind that can think at all is not speculative in some degree?)—the temptation, namely, to press known facts a little further than they will bear, when that little is all that is wanted to establish a theory.

Better to see in fevers only a certain combination of symptoms, than to run wild about a debility of the nerves, a spasm of the extreme vessels, or a peccant matter in the blood.

There is even more and more need of first specialising things into realities before fixing upon them as germs of disease.

KNOWLEDGE —

Knowledge may be an incumbrance as well as a help. Many men know more than they are able to wield. There is a point (I believe) in the acquisition of knowledge (and this point varies infinitely in different individuals), beyond which, if more be acquired, the whole mass becomes useless to its possessor.

A small overweight of knowledge is often a sore impediment to the movements of common sense.

Our knowledge is incomplete. But such as it is, we must use it; and the first condition of using it safely or profitably is to know that it is incomplete.

It is safest and best to fill up the gaps of our knowledge from analogy.

But it is a great thing, let me tell you, to understand the imperfections of our knowledge, and so to analyze its defects, as to be made aware what parts of a subject still remain (as it were) in the shade, and to be brought into clearer view by the light which future observation may bestow upon them.

There is nothing so captivating as NEW knowledge.

It would be well for those who feel strongly the desirableness of more knowledge, to consider how it is most likely to be obtained.

In the phenomena of health and of disease, there are things concerning which the present state of our knowledge is totally inadequate to explain how they are or why they are: yet of many such things we may still know more than their bare existence.

There is an use sometimes in this measuring the limits of our knowledge. In a profession like ours it is not enough to lament its imperfections. We should rather seek to understand wherein they consist, and so learn to bear with them and to make the best of them.

It is worth while to ascertain, if we can, the sources of any power we possess which results from our knowledge, and thus to obtain the surest means of still keeping it and still enlarging it.

Often, indeed, we thus feel ourselves (as it were) working with our knowledge experimentally and in detail, leaning on it, trusting it, step by step.

— AND PRETENSE

In practice there is a mischief in conceiting ourselves wiser than we are.

We cannot construct aims and indications of practice out of

hidden things, but must be content for the present to regard the whole disease as a single comprehensive indication, and so prescribe for it the single remedy and expect the cure. We shall perhaps know better some time; but no good will come from our pretending to know better now. Patience under imperfect knowledge is no proof of an unwise mind.

Then, as now, a really wise man would occasionally make shipwreck of part of his wisdom by venturing out of his depth and pretending to know more than possibly could be known.

No good ever comes from pretending to know more precision than the thing itself admits of . . .

Let him beware of that very common evil among us, the vanity of large acquaintance; of having, or affecting to have, an intimacy with everybody worth knowing. It is a vanity not fit for all men to indulge in. All cannot afford the expense of time and trouble required to keep it up.

Depend upon it, what all men indiscriminately are told they *ought* to know, all men indiscriminately will soon *pretend* to know, be it never so extravagant . . .

PREPROFESSIONAL EDUCATION

There are certain stages in the progress of any great design, at which men are apt to pause and look back upon what has been accomplished hitherto, to see if there be any errors to correct, any omissions to supply; that thus everything may be rightly ordered as they go along, and made fit and conducive to the chief end they have in view.

In universities, so that the things taught be good in them-

39

selves, education may be as miscellaneous and omnifarious and even as redundant as you please. The object is to rouse the mind and let it make acquaintance with its powers and inclinations, so that it may judge of its own natural fitness by what it is able to do the best.

The different professions have one way of glorifying themselves, which is common to all. It is by setting forth a vast array of preparatory studies, and pretending they are indispensable in order to fit a man for the simple exercise of the practical duties that belong to them.

Although I do not enumerate Latin, and Greek, and French, and Italian, and German, and insist that all these you must know, yet I by all means recommend you to get as good a literary education as you can.

Get the best scientific education you can. Let each man, according to his time and opportunities, pursue that department, or those several departments, to which his mind inclines: but let him take care to feel his ground firmly established beneath his feet as he goes along. For *here* all half knowledge is no knowledge at all.

MEDICAL EDUCATION

There is not a more difficult problem in the world than the education for a particular profession.

Have a very great care of your medical student, and how you guide him at starting. Now especially is the time for good advice, if you have any to give. Take him now into the wards of the hospital at once; fit or unfit, as people reckon fitness, thither take him. He may have learnt all sorts of things already, or he may scarcely have learnt anything at all. But as soon as you have become his masters, thither take him, and there let him remain and make it for the present his sole field of observation and thought, or curiosity, and have a guard that the best things from without do not reach him there, to his hindrance or destruction.

In laying down any scheme of education, you must take care to make it suitable to the majority of those who are to be educated. There may be circumstances in their condition and objects, rendering that education, which is the best in itself, not the best for them. Such circumstances belong, in an especial degree, to our profession. Very few enter it who are not to live by it: very few who are not required to exercise its practical duties *early,* from the necessity they are under of beginning as soon as possible to support themselves. So that the majority cannot wait to be made philosophers before they become practitioners.

If all medical students had fifteen or twenty years at their disposal, and could dedicate them all to professional education, we might pardon a little innocent declamation in displaying the rich and varied field of knowledge about to be disclosed to them; but even then, sober truth would compel us to confess that the field so pompously displayed far exceeded in extent what the best minds could hope to compass, even in fifteen or twenty years. When, however, we recollect what space of time the majority of men so addressed really can give their education, the whole affair becomes inexpressibly ludicrous.

Now I do protest, in the name of common sense, against all such proceeding as this. It is all very fine to insist that the eye cannot be understood without a knowledge of optics, nor the circulation without hydraulics, nor the bones and the muscles without mechanics: that metaphysics may have their use in leading us through the intricate functions of the nervous system, and the mysterious connection of mind and matter. It is a

41

truth; and it is a truth also that the whole circle of science is required to comprehend a single particle of matter: but the most solemn truth of all is, *that the life of man is threescore years and ten.*

Of the great cosmogony of medicine there are several departments, and each professor never fails to magnify his own, by counting the cost of time and labour, which you must be prepared to bestow if you wish to make any reasonable progress in it.

I know that much disquietude, if not unhappiness, has been felt by students, and especially by the best informed and best disposed, when, at the entrance of their profession, they have been met by obstacles which seem insurmountable.

It is the special infirmity of ingenuous minds to reflect with too much anxiety upon their own progress in knowledge; to sit in judgment upon themselves, calculating whether they have made the best of all their opportunities, and wishing, vainly wishing, that their time might come over again, to enable them to supply this omission, or rectify that mistake.

I have always thought that, in hospitals, knowledge is perpetually running to waste for want of labourers to gather it; and I think so still.

I have always thought that, in our schools, every mode of lecturing has been unduly exalted above clinical lecturing; and every place where knowledge is to be had, or is supposed to be had, has been unduly preferred to the bedside; and I continue to think thus.

I have long doubted whether systematic courses of lectures on medicine and surgery ought to be considered as essential a part of professional education as they are, and whether the rigid

42

attendance upon them which is required does not stand in the way of other more indispensable means of obtaining knowledge; and whether they are not thus in danger of becoming a serious hindrance to the very purposes they are intended to promote.

Lectures are a temptation to the more contemplative mind to learn diseases by the study of models, rather than of the things themselves. They tend to divorce him from the workshop and the chips and fragments and rude designs that lie about within it, and introduce him into a room swept and garnished and hung round with masterpieces for his contemplation. This may be all very well for gentlemen who patronize the arts; but this is not the way to make the artist.

Most properly are chemistry, and materia medica, and anatomy, taught in lecture-rooms, where the proofs are continually ready at every stage of the instruction, and the instruction itself consists in little else than exhibiting them in their proper place and order.

So pressing upon the student's mind and time is the necessity of attending a multiplicity of lectures, that he has neither attention nor leisure left to bestow upon the observation of diseases and the effects of remedies.

. . . the edicts of halls, colleges, and institutions, new and old, were rivalling one another in the ruinous amount of taxation they levied upon the time and thought of medical students, with their hundreds of lectures and inflicted upon them without mercy.

Are not medicine and surgery conversant with objects presented to the eye? and ought not they, in like manner, to be learned by the contemplation of those objects? Yes.

43

But in the lecture-room these objects cannot be constantly present, so as to keep pace with the instruction, and be appealed to as proofs. Description, therefore, is made to supply their place, and become their substitute. Description, however, is a poor substitute; for it is absolutely unintelligible, except to those who have some acquaintance with the reality.

How, then, is medical and surgical instruction to be conducted, so as to make it answer its purpose more effectually? By keeping its real objects more, and as much as possible, in view: and as those objects cannot be brought to the student, the student must be brought to them. As he cannot see them in the lecture-room, he must seek them in the wards of the hospital; and *there* he must seek his instruction too, if he is to obtain any. And even *there* he will find it difficult enough to learn, with the objects before his eyes.

I believe (what my own observation has convinced me of) that there is a mischief in putting forth a vast inventory of miscellaneous things, to be learnt by those whose times is hardly sufficient for mastering that knowledge which is obviously necessary for practical use.

For the sake of rendering the nature of disease well understood it is allowable to seize upon its simplest forms and to make much of them and to dwell long upon their explanation, before we proceed to the more complex.

CLINICAL TEACHING

When you would teach a man to read, you do not begin with the history of letters . . .

Your education is now at length concentrating itself to its great object: the time is arrived when you are to direct your minds expressly to the knowledge of diseases, and their treatment. All that you have hitherto learned in all the schools of instruction which you have frequented, you must bring with you, and make it ministerial to this knowledge. I talk not of science and philosophy only in those departments which bear immediately upon medical instruction, nor of science and philosophy only in any shape; but of everything by which your intellectual and moral nature has been cultivated and improved at any period of your lives. Every good principle received from the counsel or example of parents in your earliest years — every laudable habit derived from fortunate association with good men — every maxim of prudence and virtue from good books — and, if there be a higher source (as I trust there is), to which some of you have looked for the proper motives, and ends, and hopes and destinies of man, and really know what they are — bring these, bring all that you possess, and engage them in active exercise, and link them to the great business of your lives; for now that business may be properly said to begin. It is that by which you are to live and take your station in the world — to do good, or to do evil — to gain friends or enemies, honour or dishonour; and in which the great accountable talent committed to your use will be well or ill employed.

People do not come to read by being taught the philosophy of reading, but simply by doing the thing itself, simply by reading.

So, if you wish to teach a man medicine and its practice, you must not begin with half a dozen philosophies, or with any philosophy at all, but you must put, as it were, his alphabet into his hand at once, and bid him learn its simple characters one by one, and then help him to join them together and make the best sense of them he can.

Now your student, who is to begin in the wards of the hospital, must continue to frequent them with the mind of a learner during all the years of his pupilage.

Here is a great hospital; and here I hold that all teaching by lectures should have for its first and principle purpose to give effect to that self-teaching, which, from the objects which surround us, all may practise and profit by who have eyes and ears and a docile mind. Do not believe a word that I say until you have gone into the wards and proved it. There you will find your great book of instruction. I only pretend to supply a key, a glossary, or an index to it. Use that book as you ought, and then, though in the end you and I may have the same knowledge, it will not be because it has passed from my mind to yours, but, being gained by your own observation, ratified by your own proofs, and matured by your own thought, you will have it and hold it as your own independent possession.

. . . these Lectures . . . do not pretend to teach the clinical student any single thing peremptorily or dogmatically, but only to furnish him with certain aids and assistances by which he may be better able to teach himself.

So in entering this place, even this vast hospital, where there is many a significant, many a wonderful thing, you shall take me along with you, and I will be your guide. But it is by your own eyes, and your own minds, and (may I add) by your own hearts, that you must observe and learn, and profit: I can only point to the objects, and have little more to say than "See here, and see there."

It is your present duty to exercise your observation carefully and unremittingly; and it is my present duty to point out the fittest objects, and place them in the light in which they can be most profitably seen.

If ever the desire to view the beauties and sublimities of nature has led you to ascend some lofty eminence, you have probably taken with you one more familiar with the scene than yourselves, as a guide; but you have still trusted to your own eyes

46

and your own feelings, to fill you with the delight of the prospect, and tell you what to admire and wonder at; and you have required no more from the guide than to point with his finger, and say, "See here, and see there."

It is one thing for a man to understand a matter for himself and for his own use, and another thing to understand it and explain it for the use of others.

There are things which practical men often know assuredly, and employ successfully, yet of which they cannot convey to others either the knowledge or the use.

This I believe to be the common fault of writers and lecturers, and of all who in any manner, or anywhere, undertake to teach practical medicine, except at the bedside of the patient, that they give much too favorable a representation of their subject. And it arises after this manner. In whatever they say respecting methods of treatment, they proceed in the meanwhile upon the assumption, that they have always a good case to deal with, and are always called in at the right time. Not only do they proceed upon this assumption, but they do it without saying so.

Here I am, not so much striving to teach, as I am encouraging you to learn.

In going round the hospital my mind often reverts to the time when I was a mere beginner like yourselves; and I remember how strange and puzzling to me was everything that I saw; how I thought I never should be able to distinguish diseases, one from another, as long as I lived; and, as to treating them, I could not look forward with hope that my conscience would ever allow me to attempt any such thing.

If we consider the peculiar place which medicine holds as a department of knowledge, and how many things may be made to bear upon it which seem hardly to belong to it, no work can be too much prized which will teach us how to reason upon medical subjects, and especially how to unite the conclusions of any demonstrative experiment with the results of clinical observation, so as to render them both subservient to an explanation of diseases.

Perhaps it may appear very strange to you, that, while you are intent upon observing the symptoms of diseases and the effects of remedies, I should advise you to be very sparing in reference to books which treat expressly of such matters. You see the things themselves; then why learn them at second hand?

I would ask any person of common sense to which of the two he would submit his body with the greater confidence — to him who had Vogel, Sauvages, Cullen, or any other nosologist, by heart, or to him who, having spent a twelvemonth in the diligent observation of a great variety of diseases in a large hospital, had brought his knowledge to the test of practice during a whole month under the eye of the physician?

It has often grieved me to see young men saunter about the hospital square, with a little book in their hands, grinding a Nosology, which they are sure to forget in a few months, instead of going from bed to bed, full of interest and alacrity, and gathering knowledge which would become their own, and remain with them as long as they live.

Nosologies teach the student "Practice" in no other sense than that of enabling him to seem to have a knowledge which he has not in reality. They qualify him to pass his examination, not to understand and to treat disease.

You must go to the wards of a hospital in order to learn disease and its treatment; for there only you can see the sick man, and inquire his symptoms, and give the remedy, and note its effects, and witness its success or its failure.

When the record of the case has been read aloud, I admit you to share in my deliberation upon all its particulars, while I endeavour to assort them and bring them together, and make them yield all the light they are capable of throwing upon the nature and seat of the disease. Sometimes I can at once come to a confident diagnosis; and when I can, I at once announce what it is, and give my reasons for it . . . Sometimes, after great pains of inquiry, I am still in the dark; and when I am, I say so, and desire to reserve the case for future examination . . . Sometimes, perhaps most frequently, I feel that I have a tolerably right notion of the complaint, but require some circumstances to be more clearly made out, before I can be absolutely certain. And then I state what are the circumstances which give me the notion that I have, and what I still desiderate to bring me to a more confident conclusion.

I would wish to see the freest intercourse between pupils, with a view to mutual instruction. I would rather find two or three taking the same cases together, than one so employed alone. You have it in your power thus to give infinite help to each other.

EXAMINATIONS

The very *examinations* themselves should be conducted in the wards of the hospital.

THE PATIENT'S STORY

For practical purposes, we must often let people think and

speak of things as they seem to be, and not as they are, making a compromise between philosophy and common sense.

Thus health and sickness, and life and death, seemed the most mysterious things in the world; and the symptoms which were said to indicate them were to me a long while unintelligible.

There is such a thing as reading disease backwards . . . and a very profitable method it sometimes is. For reading it in the ordinary way we may not have made out the matter to our perfect satisfaction, and may have great need of this retrospect to elucidate it. What I mean by reading a disease backwards is, having the results before us and trying to unravel their series and sequences, and so to interpret the time of their occurrence and to assign them a relation to past events of its clinical history; to learn what took place last year or yesterday, and had a share in the process of dissolution, and what took place earlier and had to do with antecedent attacks, and what took place earlier still, and was the rudimental change which accompanied the first transition from health to disease. In this way disease is traced back from its end to its beginning by the prints or vestiges it leaves of itself during its progress.

Do we not judge of present diseases, whence they are, what they are, and whither they tend, by the nature of the coincident facts belonging to their clinical history?

If it really be fever that they have, whether their heat, cold, or perspiration, be much or little, or in whatever manner occurring, they will all testify to a consciousness of something wrong within them. What it is they feel, they cannot exactly tell. Perhaps they can say no more than that "they are ill," or "that they are downright ill."

Finding a spleen enlarged, or the liver enlarged, we have the palpable result of some morbid action; but what that morbid action has been, and whether it is still in progress (the only questions which are pathologically or practically important), we must seek to discover by other symptoms.

Think what symptoms are. They are not mere signs of the disease, but they are direct emanations from it, not things in themselves nugatory but eminently real. They are natural sensations unduly exalted or unduly depressed or variously changed or perverted. They are natural functions hurt, hindered or abolished.

———

OBSERVATION —
THE PHYSIOGNOMY OF DISEASE

The physiognomy of disease . . . can never be adequately described, and I urge you always to remark it and to dwell on it; for some acute observers have drawn such secrets from the expression of the countenance, that it has been to them in the place of almost all other symptoms.

Prior to diseases, to their diagnosis, their history, and their treatment prior to them and beyond them, there lies a large field for medical observation. It is not enough to begin with their beginning. There are things earlier than their beginning, which deserve to be known. The habits, the necessities, the misfortunes, the vices of men in society contain materials for the inquiry, and for the statistical, systematising study of physicians, fuller, far fuller of promise for the good of mankind than pathology itself.

With respect to the mode of conducting his inquiries at the bedside, I have suggested to the student how to observe and what to observe; what demands his present attention and what

51

may wait the season of his more mature experience; what books to read and what to abstain from reading; and the sort of knowledge which is principally auxiliary to clinical medicine.

Only be diligent, and, at your time of life, and in so vast a field as this hospital, the very use and exercise of observation will naturally produce a taste and tact for observing; and then whatever you see in after-life you will see with profit, and draw sound experience from it; and not only so, but you will find yourselves of kindred minds with the great masters of our art, — reading them, relishing them, and improving by them.

And, howsoever and wheresoever you learn observation, you must bring it with you into the wards of the hospital; and your observation will there breathe a spirit into it and apply it to its proper use.

I am persuaded of nothing more certainly than this, that there is a previous necessity of disciplining our own mind by an independent course of observation, in order to fit it for anything like profitable instruction by the teaching of other minds, or, indeed, to furnish us with any tolerable security against being deceived instead of being taught.

If the early habit of theorizing do not estrange the mind of the student from the wish to observe altogether, it may so pervert the faculty itself in its very use and exercise, that, be his wish what it may, he cannot observe honestly.

I am cautioning the student, the medical student especially, against trusting his mind to the fascination of any tempting theory, before he has put it fairly upon its guard by much independent observation of his own.

For how is it possible that the mind, the youthful mind especially, can bind and buckle itself to the labour of getting possession of knowledge in the hardest possible way, by sifting every particular, and by patiently observing at the bedside, when it believes itself already furnished with all the wisdom which such laborious and *jealous* processes can ever teach? Yes, observation of disease is not only a laborious but a *jealous* process: It allows nothing to pass but under the warrant of the most cautious reasoning, or of the senses themselves; for these are the natural sentinels of the truth.

The majority of medical men have no real love for the practical part of their profession. It is a labour to them to observe; therefore they are no observers. They cannot see clearly what they must strain their eyes to see at all; and I will tell you the reason of this also: it is because when they were students (pray take warning from what I say) medical practice was unpopular, and they never attended to it; and they never were able in afterlife to learn what they ought to have learnt in their youth. Their very faculty of observing was sound asleep when it should have been wide awake, and it could never afterwards be roused to discern more than the most obvious forms of things. No wonder, then, that the highest excellence in this same department of observation should have found few to appreciate it, and few to admire it.

Observation runs sadly to waste when it is made upon cases piecemeal.

For all, then, that more concerns Fever we must go and remain at the bedside and study it there. In so doing I wish we could fix the limit of speculative thought in its bearing upon practical medicine.

Upon the whole, men agree better about what is subjected to the senses than about anything else; and they agree best of all about what they see with their eyes.

53

Observation, working by itself, was able to win from the waste a large field, and to bring it into cultivation, and to reap from it a wonderful harvest. But the cultivation was expended upon the surface, and did not go deep enough into the soil.

This is the field in which ignorance and imposture reap their golden harvests. Not that it is impossible for those of good intention and good information to mistake the character of a disease, and so ascribe an efficacy to a remedy which is not its own; but those have the best security against this error who have taken the most pains to acquire a habit of faithful and jealous observation.

For it is of no use relating cases at all, unless you may take them in pieces and examine them as men do models in a workshop.

Do not let us make the difficulties of clinical observation under any circumstances greater than they are.

As diseases are better understood, and we possess surer signs for discerning their seat and progress, and events, the records of past experience become obsolete, and so a necessity arises for a new course of clinical observations.

All our knowledge was originally derived from cases. And cases must still be noted and preserved, and studied, as records of what we know, until we arrive at more general facts or principles than we have yet reached.

CONSTITUTION

What do we mean when we talk of a man's Constitution?

But it is this very thing, even a man's constitution, which fills the whole subject of practical medicine with such endless circumstances and conditions as to spoil it entirely for definition.

All intercourse with the world as it is, and acquaintance with contemporary men, all study of history and of the characters of men still traceable upon its pages, would lead to the conclusion that never, from the foundation of the world until now, have there existed two individuals who, in outward presentment and in intellectual and moral attributes, were the exact counterparts of each other.

The realities, which these portentous terms, temperament, idiosyncrasy, susceptibility, diathesis represent, are nothing less than a man's constitution, or the individuality of his physical and vital nature, and its dstribution into certain species which are to be understood but not defined.

A man's physical individuality may be written in a much smaller character, or in a character legible only by the physician, and not always by him, but only as circumstances chance to bring it out, and put it in points of view that make it visible. Yet this smaller thing, seen but by the physician, and by him occasionally and seldom, being, however, and undoubted reality, may become a vast event in its practical bearing and use.

Practically, he has been turning away from the disease, and fixing his attention almost or altogether upon the patient who suffers it. He has been studying an individual constitution; and studying it under the surest test and trial that can be conceived of all its living powers.

The older we get, and the more conversant we have become with diseases, patients, and remedies, the more stress do we find ourselves laying upon a man's constitution.

MIND, BODY AND SPIRIT

Every day brought some fresh proof how great was the influence of mental distress in augmenting bodily pain and sickness. Whatever circumstances were calculated to make a strong impression upon the spirits, threw them back at once from a state of convalescence, into absolute disease.

Whenever, therefore, an individual was pardoned, all the rest were thrown into agony of the bitterest disappointment, and were, at the same time, overtaken by disease. It was not a mere nervous or hysterical ailment, but some actual form of real disease, such as they have before suffered, and requiring the strictest medical treatment for its relief.

Now the will, I fear, is far less master of the mind than of the body. A man may resolve never to move from his chair, but he cannot resolve never to be angry.

Passions and affections of the mind are wont to show their power over the body especially by the manner in which they influence the heart, even the healthy heart; rousing it to tumultuous and irregular action and engendering pain within it.

DIAGNOSIS

The diagnosis of disease is often easy, often difficult, and often impossible.

Of the signs by which physicians become acquainted with diseases in the living body, some are expressive of their nature, and some are expressive only of the parts they occupy. The first flow directly from their essence and may be called essential symptoms: the second are derived from the disturbed functions and sensations of particular organs, and may be called accidental. This distinction between essential and accidental symptoms is one of great practical importance.

Ordinary diseases will sometimes occur under extraordinary circumstances, or in unusual situations; and then we are apt to be thrown out in our diagnosis, as the pilot is in his course upon any unexpected alteration of lights and signals on the coast. He makes false points, and so do we.

The general vascular system and the general nervous system serve each as a glass in which we are fain to read the reflection of diseases, when we have no direct vision of the diseases themselves. Here, as in higher philosophies, we take measure of things by their shadows.

In every disease seek to come at the purely diagnostic symptoms if you can, and put a high value upon them. But do not imagine that other symptoms have no value at all. You learn the diseases in its essence and seat from its diagnostic symptoms. But other symptoms commonly tell you of its magnitude, and of its probable event; other symptoms sometimes become the guide of its treatment.

To come at the real origin of any symptom, it is necessary to ascertain what is the simplest form of disease with which it is apt to be associated.

Auscultation brought to them a new light and a new interest. And then these same became the cases which we were continually busy about, which we were never tired of visiting and examining and ausculting, and of examining and ausculting again and again; and so comparing our clinical observation during life with the disclosures of morbid anatomy after death we became vain of our often-verified diagnosis.

You may listen to the chest for ever and be no wiser, if you do not previously know what it is you are to hear. You may beat the chest for ever, and all in vain, unless you know what it is that is capable of rendering it now dull and now resonant.

It is an important truth well worthy of being remembered, that diagnosis is capable of being greatly aided or greatly obstructed by the *personal character* of the patient. Education, and the better habits of civilized life, render men more rationally attentive to their internal sensations and better able to describe them; whereas over refinement engenders such excessive care and regard of the feelings, that it contrives to sophisticate and spoil them; and barbarity acts so much in spite of them, that it blunts or nearly abolishes them altogether.

Organs must be previously sound to show clearly the nature of the injury or malady which they suffer, and that, in proportion as they are unsound, they are spoiled for giving true expression to the ills which afterwards befall them.

Surely a lasting debt of gratitude is due from mankind to those who shall discover an unerring sign of any disease. The more so, if the disease be of a formidable nature. The more so still, if the sign declare the disease early enough to bring our knowledge of its existence fairly within the period that will allow it to be successfully treated by medicine.

The eye, the ear, and every sense and faculty, which can convey intelligence of what goes on within a man should be kept upon the watch.

Where, then, lay the secret of our former ignorance and of our present knowledge? Let us try to trace it out; and in so doing, we shall see what time, what instruments, and what happy opportunities, are all needed to perfect the diagnosis of an internal disease.

58

But how much soever physicians may learn from what constitutes the physiognomy of diseases in its largest sense (and, indeed, they may learn a great deal), their more accurate knowledge is derived from symptoms which admit of a more exact analysis.

In that complex of action and suffering which belongs to injury and disease, small things and great, accidents and essentials, are often so crowded together as to defy analysis, and causes and effects get so mixed that one can hardly tell which is which.

It is by symptoms, and by symptoms only, that we can learn the existence, and seat, and nature, of diseases in the living body, or can direct and methodize their treatment.

PROGNOSIS

I wish I had none of these unexpected issues to tell you of. They must disappoint your calculations, and disturb your satisfaction, just when you were, perhaps, beginning to look with complacency on the happy results of certain straightforward methods of practice which dealt in simple and powerful means, and fulfilled plain and intelligible indications, and were said to do their work, upon the whole, quickly and successfully.

The sum of our experience carefully reckoned is consistent enough, upon the whole, to allow of our making fair anticipation of the course of diseases, and of the effects of remedies in particular cases. Without this there could hardly be a rational practice of medicine at all.

Still of the simplest disease and their course, and of the simplest remedies and their effects, our experience is not uniform enough to make sure of events, and excuse us from attentively watching all cases.

There is no such thing as calculating the results of medical treatment with certainty. Success and failure run contrary to expectation sometimes in every disease.

TREATMENT

It is an instructive fact that, as the knowledge of disease has increased, the practice of medicine has been less and less conversant with cures and more and more conversant with treatment.

Let cure be looked upon as concerned with the disease as such, and having little or no regard to the individual patient whom it befalls. Treatment is concerned with the individual patient and leaves his disease to take care of itself.

In the meantime, perhaps, he willingly admits the use of other medicines for good but subordinate purposes; it may be as helps and auxiliaries, it may be for comfort's sake, or it may be for the prejudice's sake of patients or friends, which it is innocent, or wise and needful, to satisfy.

To bring many important remedies together, and unite them by a lucky combination, and compress them within a small compass, and so place them within the common reach, all this gives a facility of prescribing which is hurtful to the advance of medical experience. The facility of prescribing is a temptation to prescribe; and, under this temptation, there is a lavish expenditure continually going on of important remedies in the mass, of which the prescribers have made no sufficient experiment in detail.

To scatter above twenty remedies, and to let hit which may, is like pigeon-shooting in companies. The bird falls; but whose gun was it that brought it down? Nobody is reputed the better marksman after a hundred volleys.

To know the import of single indications and the power of single remedies lies at the root of all sound practice; and I am persuaded that no man can clearly see and prosecute many indications together, or can safely and successfully use many remedies together, who has not begun by studying both indications and remedies one by one.

It is not possible that the treatment of diseases shall be ever set at rest by the consent of physicians, or that fixed and uniform plans and remedies shall ever be adopted in cases bearing the same nosological name and character.

I conceive it hardly possible for a physician to employ his time worse than in quest of new specifics. His common sense would be about equal to that of the man who should trust his hopes of growing rich to the chance of finding a bag of money. But a specific medicine is an excellent thing, and so is a bag of money; and, being found, it is worth the study of a life to turn them both to all the good purposes of which they are capable.

With respect to the influence of external agents as remedies, I would recommend you to be most jealously observant of every circumstance connected with the treatment of individual cases. A mere sequence of events is not a necessary sequence. The remedy may be administered, and the disease may cease; and yet the treatment and the cure may not be cause and effect.

You cannot be sure of the success of your remedy, while you are still uncertain of the nature of the disease.

Beware of mistaking the nature of the disease, and then be-

61

lieving that the remedy has cured what in fact never existed.

You would not sacrifice men's lives to the vanity of diagnosis. The auscultatory signs, when they come, will only serve to localise the disease. Its nature is plain enough already; and we treat *its nature,* and not *its seat.*

There is a lesson which we are apt to learn slowly, but which all of us come to learn at last. It is this—that while present pain and present peril call loudest for relief and rescue, still in relieving and rescuing, the ultimate well-being of the patient must not be disregarded altogether.

As the disease may have an essential element beyond its sensible actions and sufferings, so the remedies may have secret operations beyond those which are seen and palpable.

Let it be observed, however, that any remedy which, working in the dark, is nevertheless trusted for its ultimate effects, requires to be administered with the greatest of care.

Further, we are thus often able to survey retrospectively (and it is a most profitable exercise) the course and management of particular cases, and their results; and see where we have done well, and where we have done ill; where, from treatment perfectly carried out in all its details, restoration has followed as the natural and necessary consequence; or where, from mischance or mismanagement, from defect or misuse of knowledge in this or that practical detail, restoration has been postponed, or left imperfect, or has failed altogether.

In my time Medicine has been going through a speculative crisis of two opposite kinds by turns; and strength (so-called) has ruled one, and weakness the other. Beyond all question, during its critical ascendancy, abstract strength cost the world many lives by its practice of blood-letting; and abstract weakness, in its turn, has cost the world many also by its practice of brandy-giving. I have not statistics to show with exactness which of the two has levied the larger mortal tax upon mankind. My impression is that the bad pre-eminence belongs to the latter.

Take pneumonia. It has been treated by bleeding, and got well. It has been treated by brandy, and got well. It has been left to itself, and got well. And the bleeders, the brandy-givers, and the doers of nothing at all, respectively, have had a vast deal to say for themselves and against their rivals. And which of them are to be our guides and masters in the treatment of pneumonia? None of them for a single day, much less for always.

Choose almost any febrile disease you please, and question the experience of honest and well-informed physicians about it, and what it was, and how it was best treated at their own time and place of observation; and you will find them tolerably well agreed. But take this experience and agreement of theirs to determine its nature absolutely, and fix the canon of its treatment for all places and all times, and you will run into a great practical delusion.

Opium once given is gone beyond your power to recall.

When, in the confusion and tumult of disease, life has been poised, as it were, on a pin's point, and a single effort of skill has saved it, the exploit speaks great things for the glory of our art and its simple methods.

There was formerly an evident industry for combining in the remedy whatever was thought to be of virtue for each of the symptoms which constituted the disease. Hence, various nostrums were in daily use containing twenty or thirty ingredients. But, in our days, a remedy of two or three ingredients — often, indeed, of a single article — is safely trusted for treating diseases of complex and multifarious symptoms.

Remedies are our great analysers of disease.

It is beyond question that the adoption of special remedies for diseases upon insufficient grounds is a main hindrance to practical medicine.

An uncomfortable sort of suspicion possesses me that physicians from time immemorial have prescribed, and still go on prescribing remedies, upon the credit they have got of curing particular diseases, without the least reasonable evidence that the remedies ever did anything of the sort.

Hence nothing is more certain than that numerous articles still encumber our materia medica, and still pass for being able to do something or other extraordinary, simply on account of the infinite time and trouble that would be needed to prove them utterly worthless.

To make the heart beat slower by digitalis, and so believe oneself remedying consumption, is about as wise as it would be to think of improving the weather by playing tricks with the barometer, or altering the real time of day by tampering with the clock.

Verily, there is nothing so self-deceiving and evasive, and upon the whole so mischievous, as to this love of specific remedies. It is akin to the love of the marvelous.

Poisons and medicine are oftentimes the same substances given with different intents.

Specifics or special remedies always seem to me to contain within them a promise of prophecy of future knowledge, wait-

64

ing for time and opportunity and suitable minds to work it out.

Now it strikes one that we should be able to make a better use of specifics or special remedies if we knew more about them; if we could raise the curtain a little, and catch a glimpse of them at work in some positive manner; if we could discern them doing something conducive to the ultimate end for which we give them.

We must not make our ignorance of how the special remedy cures a bar to our use of it.

But neither scientific experiment upon the thing itself (quinine), nor trial of its remedial effects during two hundred years, has enabled us to catch a glimpse of it actually at work. It increases nothing, and diminishes nothing. It neither evacuates not restrains. It has to do neither with bile, or with urine or saliva; nor with any special secretion. It neither directly soothes nor directly stimulates. It neither puts to sleep nor keeps awake. It works the cure; but it does nothing, as far as we see, prior, preparatory, and intermediate to the cure it works.

How mercury makes the bile to flow, or how opium brings quiet and sleep, I do not know; but my experience trusts them for these effects; and these effects are in my hands preparatory to the successful management of many forms of disease.

For the *treatment* of acute rheumatism, above all other diseases which can be named, is a thing to put the physician and medicine itself to the trial of what they can really do. There are no specifics at hand.

At length this small ray of truth found me out in the dark; viz. that some medicines were remedial simply by bringing diseases to an end without any intermediate operation being apparent, or intended, or thought of; and that some were remedial

by bringing diseases indeed to an end, but not without intermediate operations, both apparent and designed, and looked for
as conditional to the result.

But medicine contemplates other objects besides cure. It
aims still to postpone the progress of incurable disease and to
put off its evil consequences; and, when, they can be no longer
postponed, it seeks to render them more tolerable.

In the treatment of disease our business is with the individual, and our experience of the many goes to fit us for our
dealings with the one. Yet it may not exactly fit us. But if to it be
added a prior experience, had of the individual now the subject
of treatment, then it becomes a perfect experience, and as nearly infallible as the nature of the things to which it is applied will
allow it to be.

But the highest office of medicine is to minister to diseases,
which, by themselves or by their incidents, go directly and rapidly to the destruction of life. And this is not to be done by beg-
ging people to be reasonable and abstain from what is wrong,
and cheating and cajoling them into compliance. But it is a business for wise and cautious men alone to meddle with.

But inasmuch as injurious things are commonly very pleasant things, people are reluctant to leave them off at our mere
bidding. Hence in this, which is their humblest province, small
credit upon the whole has been gained by the best physicians.
The advice they have to give is much too simple for the world
to accept upon the credit and character of well instructed and
honest men.

There is nothing edible or potable in the world, which has
not found somebody or other to eat it or drink it as a sovereign
remedy for some disease, and upon recommendation of some
physician.

66

THE ENQUIRING MIND —

A THERAPEUTIC STORY

A gentleman went from Scotland to consult a celebrated watering-place physician. His complaint was asthma. A scheme of diet was laid down for him, scrupulously and minutely strict; and he followed it to the letter. A mixed multitude of medicines was prescribed for him, which had an unpromising look of strife and incongruity. But he took them all bravely and obediently. And verily he had his reward. He obtained relief of his asthma. But the asthma would still return; and, as often as it returned, he betook himself to his dietetic and remedial discipline, and it went away again; and so his faith was confirmed. In process of time, however, whether the diet was too austere or the medicine too nauseous, and so the flesh began to rebel, or whether a laudable curiosity set him to find out the secret of his treatment and relief, he certainly began to question the necessity of *all* the means to the end. So, on his next attack, adhering to his dietetic rules, he bravely took no physic. But the asthma bided, and would not leave him until he had recourse to his accustomed medicines. On the following attack, he set at nought his dietetic rules, and scrupulously took his physic; and the asthma passed away as usual.

It was pretty plain that the physic-bottle contained the cure. But to which of the many ingredients did it belong? To one or two or three, or to the whole hotch-potch working mysteriously together for good? In a matter which so nearly concerned him, the patient might be pardoned for laying his rash analytical hands upon the mysterious mixture. It contained, among twenty other things, a few grains of iodide of potassium. Ingredient after ingredient was deducted; and simpler and simpler as the mixture became, it still had equal power to abate the asthma, until the iodide of potassium was deducted in its turn, and then its sovereign power was gone. Again, all the ingredients were tried, excepting only the iodide of potassium; but altogether they did not touch the asthma remedially. Finally, every other ingredient was excluded, and the iodide left alone; and alone it displayed a sovereign remedial power.

VACCINATION —
A PREVIEW OF VIRUSES

We take something on a pin's point, and with that pin's point we just prick the skin hardly enough to be felt or seen. But by this little prick the something has gained its entrance, and is gone its way whither within the living body we do not exactly know. They say it has gone at once into the blood, has mingled with it, and is already distributed with it everywhere. Indeed one can hardly believe otherwise. But wherever the thing be gone, and whether moving or stationary, we can find it no more. Still wait for a certain time, a time forereckoned from the known quality of the thing upon the pin's point; wait, and a disease will come forth forereckoned also from the very same thing, a disease having its own proper characteristics and different from all other diseases in the world.

This primary element in producing its disease multiplies itself into new material elements which are divisible to infinity and separable from their own living body, their native body (so to speak), and ready to be transferred to other living bodies innumerable, and so to bring vast communities into the same conditions of disease.

DISEASES

Diseases are not abstractions; they are modes of acting, different from the natural and healthy modes — modes of disor-

68

ganizing, modes of suffering, and modes of dying; and there must be a living, moving sentient body for all this.

This body must be your study, and your continual care — your active, willing, earnest care. Nothing must make you shrink from it. In its weakness and infirmities, in the dishonours of its corruption, you must still value it — still stay by it — to mark its hunger and thirst, its sleeping and waking, its heat and its cold; to hear its complaints, to register its groans.

And is it possible to feel interest in all this? Ay, indeed is it; a greater, far greater, interest than ever painter or sculptor took in the form and beauties of its health.

Whence comes this interest? At first, perhaps, it seldom comes naturally; a mere sense of duty must engender it; and still, for a while, a mere sense of duty must keep it alive. Presently, the quick, curious, restless spirit of science enlivens it; and then it becomes an excitement, and then a pleasure, and then the deliberate choice of the mind.

Fever is not the man's disease, but his life assailed by his disease; even his life on a large scale.

Diseases are irremediable in two senses; either nature wants the power, or we want the remedy. The essential work, or operative process of reparation, belongs to nature. Medicine only furnishes inducements or removes impediments. Failure may be on the part of one or the other, or of both.

In truth, the amount of irremediable disease in the world is enormous.

For diseases may bear diverse names according to the parts and organs which they occupy, and still have a kindred nature and acknowledge a common origin.

69

The living disease, while it works its own changes in the part it occupies, gives and receives influences and impressions to and from other parts, and to and from the constitution at large.

Disease is a series of new and extraordinary actions. Each link in the series is essential to the integrity of the whole. Let one link be fairly broken, and this integrity is spoiled; and there is an end of the disease; and then the constitution is left to resume its old and accustomed actions, which are the actions of health.

The physician pursues the disease through its own channels. He tracks it to its springhead, and takes hold of it there, and puts an end to it.

Disease is a great physiological teacher. Perhaps it is the greatest of all. It institutes experiments which we cannot imitate, and so tells us many things which, but for it, we should never know.

CHRONIC DISEASES

When the question is of chronic disease a single case proves nothing.

Our knowledge of chronic maladies is picked up piecemeal from numerous cases seen for a while, and only for a while, at different periods of their progress.

There is that in the nature of chronic disease, which makes it only half disclose itself. It discloses itself only in its results, and not in its operations. Whereas acute disease discloses itself in both.

How rarely has it happened to any of us to have numerous

70

individuals the subjects of any given chronic disease, so constantly within our reach, that we could see them and inquire into their condition two or three times a year, for many years together, or for the whole of their lives!

Our own lives must needs last for many generations to furnish us an experience of other men's diseases in their entire course, which last half or the whole of theirs.

When disease is essentially chronic, the preceding circumstances conducive to it are (so to speak) chronic also. They are often covert and far-fetched and hard to unravel, and we must often look back to a man's whole life, or to the life of his progenitors, before we find them.

In proportion as diseases are more chronic, they are, upon the whole, less easily assigned to their external exciting causes. With respect to them, a longer experience and inquiry are needed to establish a uniform sequence of the events.

The power of medicine over chronic disease is a thing hard to get at and appreciate justly.

PAIN

It would be a great thing to understand Pain in all its meanings.

The first thing to be noticed is the difficulty we have in judging of Pain as a symptom which we do not find in respect of other symptoms.

No man, wise or foolish, ever suffered Pain, who did not invest it with a quasi materialism.

71

I have known many a philosopher, outreasoned by his feelings, take to rating and chiding *his Pain,* as if it were an entity or quiddity of itself.

Then, admitting our patient honest and his Pain real, how are we to make sure of its degree?

In matters of feeling we must depend entirely upon what our patient tells us. Every man smarts with his own pain; himself, and nobody else, can say how much.

Not only degrees of pain, but its existence, in any degree, must be taken upon the testimony of the patient.

Whatever sick-bed we stand by, and hear severe Pain complained of, and find it the accompaniment of febrile or sudden or rapidly progressive disease, we must not leave that bedside until we have satisfied ourselves whether anything, or what, is to be done expressly for the Pain.

Pain may kill. It may overwhelm the nervous system by its mere magnitude and duration.

The sense of pain is in proportion to the magnitude of the disease only within certain limits. The extremity of the disease may abate or even abolish the sense of pain altogether.

Pain, itself a thing of life, can only be tested by its effects upon life, and the functions of life. And whether it be small or great (so to speak), or of whatever degree, it is to its effect upon life and the functions of life that we must look, if we would know the part it acts pathologically, and what it requires remedially in individual cases.

Think of the world of Pain that has been spared by the use of chloroform!

RHEUMATISM

Times without number, we have met with chronic valvular disorganizations which might have, and probably had, their origin in some attack of endocarditis, which was never known, and never treated.

Who shall say that the arthritic inflammation and the cardiac inflammation, and the fever itself, with its profuse and sour-smelling perspirations, and the urine, loaded with lithates and red colouring matter, do not all spring from some noxious principle formed in, or finding its way into, the blood, this last containing, in truth, the essence of the disease?

The disease cannot be named which makes a handsomer figure nosologically than this Rheumatism.

But what this thing is, which, favoured by coincidents or by its own sole agency, is the very cause of Rheumatism, no man knows.

Remember acute rheumatism is (if we may so speak pathologically) the great parent root of inflammations of the heart.

Acute rheumatism has experienced strange things at the hands of medical men. No disease has been treated by such various and opposite methods.

Where the constitution of the patient is habitually cachectic, and he has no natural health to oppose to the casual incursions of disease, if that disease be acute rheumatism your treatment is apt to fail.

The poor are the most frequent subjects of acute rheumatism . . .

73

Whoever has had his heart once inflamed (whether it be the endocardium or pericardium which is the seat of disease) and left thenceforth permanently unsound, may have it inflamed again . . .

The circumstances of half a man's life may have a bearing upon his present disease(they indeed often have upon the secondary inflammation of the heart) and, when you come to set them forth, you seem rather to be telling a story than relating a case.

ANGINA PECTORIS

This angina, this mixture of the sharpest pain with a feeling of instant death, has its seat in the upper, middle or lower part of the sternum; it passes through the chest to the spine, often inclining more to the left than to the right side. It comes suddenly and goes suddenly. This is all which constantly belongs to the disease.

None can well describe the quality of a pain but those who have felt it. And the subjects of angina pectoris report, that it is a suffering as sharp as any that can be conceived in the nature of pain, and that it includes moreover something which is beyond the nature of pain, a sense of dying.

There is a strength and a prevalency in the pain of angina pectoris which nothing but opium has the power to master.

The patient by his own experience finds out unerringly what in himself is the immediately exciting cause of the paroxysm of angina pectoris.

TUBERCULOSIS

There are many strange things respecting Pulmonary Consumption — many striking discrepancies between case and case, and many contrarieties of opinion among the well-informed as to its proper mode of treatment, — which, heretofore, the best of us have been unable to reconcile or explain.

And we can say that there are cases essentially phthisical in which the disease accomplishes its course, as it were, by parts and parcels; many times apparently beginning, and many times apparently ending, but always (as far as I see) beginning again: a year or two of disease, a year or two of health, then a year or two of disease again. Yet, upon these terms, I have known those who have passed neither a short nor a useless, nor an unhappy life. I have known those who have so gathered up the fragments of their broken health as to make them serve for high and useful purposes, and put to shame the fewer and smaller performances of stronger men.

Let me guard you against a vulgar error. Haemoptysis and rupture of a blood-vessel are, in the popular sense, convertible terms; so much is one conceived to be the natural and necessary consequence of the other. But rupture of a blood-vessel which has been esteemed the only cause of Haemoptysis, is unquestionably the rarest cause of all; and this accident, which one might expect to find frequent in Pulmonary Consumption, nature has taken great pains to guard against; for no sooner does the destructive process of forming Vomicae within the lungs begin, than she sedulously betakes herself to closing up the arteries which lead to them by clots of blood: and as to the veins, partly (I believe) by the same process, and by otherwise arresting the circulation through them, she reduces them to impervious shreds.

To the question posed with such intent, it is a mockery to

answer "Consumption is a curable disease;" because, forsooth, its entire process from beginning to end — its formation, progress, cure — may be secretly transacted within the body without our knowing or suspecting any thing about it.

Finally, then, Pulmonary Consumption is no more than a fragment of a great constitutional malady, which it would be in vain to think of measuring by the stethoscope, and which it belongs to a higher discipline than any mere skill in Auscultation rightly to comprehend.

I do not wish you to fasten on small points, and swell them into importance, and by refining and sophisticating to make something out of nothing at all, and frighten families, and deceive yourselves into a belief that you have cured Consumption.

DIETARY DEFICIENCY DISEASE

In regard to such diseases, especially, as are engendered by defective nutrition, we knew it to be a matter of experience, that they are generally capable of being speedily and effectually cured by an improved diet.

With regard to the diet of prisoners undergoing punishment for crimes, we presume the object to be, that they should have enough for nourishment and health, and nothing more. How much, and what quality of food will actually suffice for this purpose, can be deduced only from numerous and careful experiments. But no such experiments, as far as we know, have ever been made.

SCURVY

In many who exhibited specks and spots only of ecchymosis,

and in all whose limbs were covered with large blotches, the muscles of the legs were perfectly hard and rigid. In a few, the legs were oedematous, and one man was universally dropsical.

The gums had a purplish hue, and were tender and sore, and often ragged, just where they come in application with the teeth.

INFLAMMATION

Inflammation is, pre-eminently, a fundamental subject of practical medicine, and its great vital ingredient is its Fever. It is to us a sort of grammar which helps us to construe half the things we see and deal with as physicians.

MIGRAINE

What a crowd of symptoms go to make up that best known and most distressing of all remedial maladies, the sick headache!

ASTHMA

Fortunate the man who can get rid of an asthmatic attack on any terms ...

INTERSTITIAL EMPHYSEMA OF THE LUNG

The Emphysema from Dilatation or Rupture of the air-cells is a chronic affection resulting from causes which are tardy in

77

their operation; but the interlobular Emphysema takes place in a moment, and is the result of accident. Any violent effort which holds or intercepts the breath may cause it; the striving or parturition, the straining to unload the bowels, or to lift a heavy weight. I have myself seen it produced by the convulsive struggle of whooping cough; at least I presume so: for I have seen the subcutaneous cellular tissue about the neck of a child become blown up with air after a fit of coughing; but this happened before I had Auscultation to help me in inquiring into the condition of the lungs.

From the manner in which the interlobular partitions run parallel to each other, it must be obvious that, when several are infiltrated with air at once, there will result a separation of various pulmonary lobules entirely from each other, like little islets.

When this interlobular Emphysema is near the root of the lungs, it soon reaches the mediastinum, whence air escapes into the cellular texture of the whole body.

RARE DISEASES

Some forms of disease are so rare, that if all the experience of them which there is in the world were put together and possessed by one man, it would not make him very wise upon the matter.

Extraordinary cases are often merely curious, and interesting only because they are curious. But sometimes they are interesting because they furnish rare and fortunate opportunities of instruction, filling up gaps in our knowledge, or fortifying it with new proofs, and so giving it a higher degree of certainty than it had before.

A single entire case often furnishes the key to many fragments of cases.

Nevertheless, what is occasional only and extraordinary is sometimes as a light let in from a new quarter, and bringing into view what would otherwise have lain hid.

SPECIALIZATION

The study of our times has been chiefly to specialize and to localize disease, and it has had very useful results. But it has had a tendency to narrow our views, and to cripple our practice by setting up as many several pathologies within the body as there are several organs.

The very habit of dwelling long and minutely (as we need must if we would understand them) upon the facts which concern the pathology of the one organ has brought us consciously to regard it as a single center of disease much more than it really is.

In proportion as we are more intent upon investigating the local processes of diseases in a particular organ, scrutinizing them pathologically, and nicely weighing their diagnostic signs, there is a danger that our minds may be withdrawn from those larger views which regard their constitutional origin, and their consequent liability to fall upon any or all organs of the body.

THE HEART

There is no organ of the body which during life submits its structural condition so freely to our knowledge as the Heart.

The Heart using its proper language of sounds and impulses, how clearly and emphatically does it speak of its own diseases to the ear and touch of experience.

Observation has traced back, with fearful fidelity, a long line of formidable and fatal diseases to their pathological parentage in the heart.

In speculating upon diseases and disorganisations of other parts as the causes conducive to disease and disorganisations of the heart, we must be cautious that we do not invert the real order of things. For the order of causation will be found to run as often from the heart to other organs as from other organs to the heart.

In every organ of the body, and pre-eminently in the Heart, the living actions and sufferings of disease have a compass and a reach far beyond its material framework.

Only consider for a moment the proper office of the valves. They are meant (as it were) to keep guard at the orifices of the heart, and throw them wide open to the onward course of the blood, and hold them close-barred against its refluent current. But disease spoils their fitness sometimes for this office, and sometimes for that.

Valvular disease on the right side of the heart alone is a most rare occurrence; and, when it is found on both sides together, the disease on the left generally so far outruns that on the right, as to have reached its acme before the other has hardly begun.

Strange things happen to the heart when the chest is deformed.

Deformity of the chest, resulting from curvature of the spine is justly reckoned among the causes capable of producing disorganisation of the heart, especially active or passive dilatation; or, it may be, dilatation both of one kind and the other co-existing in the several cavities of the same heart. The whole chest being distorted and narrowed, and the lungs straitened and imprisoned, and the heart itself displaced and the aorta tortuous, and the liver bearing hard with its external pressure, lead upon the whole to as large an amount of hurtful encroachment of organ upon organ as can possibly be conceived. And this encroachment cannot be without mechanical impediment; and this impediment cannot be without hurt and hindrance, first, to the functions, and then to the structure of such organs as the heart and lungs.

Because inflammation of the heart tends to a destructive disorganization, every day that it is allowed to abide and continue its progress, the heart sustains more and more injury from morbid matter deposited upon it or within it, and its functions are hindered and baffled, and at last abolished; and these functions are vital.

. . . one principal object I have in view is to bring diseases of the heart to a living test; to stand by the bed-side, and there see how much we know of them, and how much we conjecture, and how, according to degrees of probability, our conjecture is made, sometimes little less than knowledge, and sometimes little more than a guess. Now we are able during life to conjecture a fat heart with such strength of probability that we almost know it.

By what agency does the heart become disorganized in consequence of a dilated aorta? It is, probably, by its own extraordinary efforts to overcome a virtual impediment to the circulation. Blood being immediately poured from it into a larger space than natural, requires from the heart an augmentation of its motive impulse.

Subjects of asthmatic disease furnish the most frequent instances of dilatation of the heart from causes seated in the lungs.

What exact relation disease of the kidneys bears to hypertrophy of the heart, we do not know even yet. But the two

81

are too often coincident in the same subjects for them not to bear some, and that a very important, relation to each other.

The plainest and most palpable effects of an unsound heart upon the circulation in the veins are denoted by their distended and overloaded state.

Nature does, as it were, make use of the lungs as the readiest and the nearest channel through which to relieve the oppression of the heart.

It would be difficult to overrate the value, as guides to practice, of the signs which declare themselves through the medium of the lungs in every case of unsound heart.

What can be said of palpitations of the heart, and intermissions, and irregularities of its beats, which come and go during a man's whole existence, neither originating in any known disease, nor terminating in any, nor abridging in any measure the duration of life.

A little edema of the ankles . . . is the earliest beginning of serous effusion, which may go on increasing until it has pervaded the entire cellular structure and filled every serous cavity of the body.

There are no certain measures of pain, of palpitation, and irregular action, annexed to a given amount of unsoundness in the heart.

The heart that has a valve thickened and an orifice contracted, or its pericardium adherent, is apt to suffer pain, and to palpitate and beat out of time.

Learn, then, to read aright the meaning of these two orders of symptoms referable to the heart, — the vital and the mechanical.

82

I would state then summarily, that it belongs to the heart, in its different states of permanent unsoundness, sometimes to affect the brain perilously or fatally, the brain itself being altogether free from disease; and sometimes only to bring disease, which already exists within the brain, sooner, and more inevitably, to a perilous and fatal event. The work may be entirely of the heart, or it may be shared between the heart and the brain.

The man, who, having an unsound heart, must traffic with his sinews, for his daily bread, has a poor chance of benefit from medicine.

What a gain will it be to mankind, should observation hereafter discover that the conversion of the valves of the heart, and the lining of arteries, into earthy matter or cartilage, has its sure pathological origin in certain forms of disease in other parts, or in the constitution at large, which are both obvious and curable, or in certain habits and modes of living which can be rectified or avoided!

HEART SOUNDS AND MURMURS

The sounds which naturally accompany the movements of the healthy heart, can only be learnt by the practice of listening to them. It is useless to describe them.

Murmurs are to be caught quickly, and distinguished surely, and turned to a ready use, only by practice.

The ear must be a well-educated and well-practiced ear, or it is not a trustworthy witness.

In proportion as the sounds of the healthy heart are more

highly intonated, they acquire a greater audible extent. The louder they are, the further you hear them.

The abnormal murmurs, as well as the natural sounds, of the heart, are heard to a greater distance in proportion to their mere loudness, and that not only in the direction to which the current of the blood conducts them, but in all directions.

Thus the disease and the impediment still increasing may, and sometimes do, reach a point at which the endocardial murmur eases thenceforth, and altogether, as long as life remains.

As to the *sounds* themselves, since the ear can only become familiar with them by practice, I leave you to be your own instructors. As to their theory, taking the matters of fact and matters of speculation which have been brought to bear upon it, I consider that it is in part satisfactorily made out, and in part only plausibly surmised.

If in a healthy man we carry bleeding far enough to blanch the surface of the body, we create an audible systolic murmur in the precordial region, and diffuse it through the arteries.

Place the instrument upon the neck by the side of the trachea, and pretty close to it, and at the same time rest your finger upon the space between the angle of the jaw and the mastoid process; and when your ear has caught a continuous humming sound, and listened for a while and made sure of it, then press your finger firmly down upon the vein, and the sound, if it be the true venous murmur, will immediately cease; then raise your finger, and if it be the true venous murmur it will immediately return.

A very free current of blood is essential to the production of the venous murmur.

Never omit to listen to the praecordial region whenever you

visit a case of acute rheumatism, and visit a case of acute rheumatism oftener perhaps than you otherwise would do merely for the sake of so listening.

The short physiological account of auscultation, which has just been given, will probably be found useful to us as we proceed. At all events we may make a platform of it, where we think it will bear us, and tread more cautiously upon it, where we think it will not.

THE PULSE

The oracle of old made it the top of wisdom to know one's self, but did not fix the credit due to that fragment of self-knowledge which enables a man to keep count of his own pulse.

Surely the number of the *pulse* ought to have a vast deal to teach us, seeing what a point we make of ascertaining it in every instance. The pulling out of the watch, and the deliberation which follows, must appear to the patient at least the most solemn part of the interview with his physician.

THE EYE

If you desire to make pathological knowledge the groundwork of your credit and usefulness through life, let me advise you not to allow the period of your pupilage to pass by without making a special study of the diseases of the *eye*. Here you see almost all diseases in miniature; and from the peculiar structure of the eye, you see them as through a glass; and you learn many of the little wonderful details in the nature of morbid processes, which, but for the observation of them in the eye, would not

85

have been known at all. Let every one of you who has a few months to spare give them to the Eye Infirmary.

The eye might have been intended to furnish us a little model for studying processes of disease and processes of reparation as they go on in all parts of the body, so admirable does it answer this purpose.

───※───

ABOUT MUSCLES

How strangely covert and secret and beyond the reach of clinical observation are all the chief diseases and injuries which primarily affect the muscular structure.

───※───

PATHOLOGY

Pathology is a study of your whole life.

Whatever is learned by dissection, concerning forms and structures; whatever by chemistry, concerning elementary constituents; whatever by experiment, concerning the appearance and behaviour of parts and organs, under any new conditions in which they are artificially placed; and finally, whatever is learned concerning the acting and sufferings of disease in the living man; all these, in their sum aggregate, must be deemed to constitute one *pathology*.

You must study inflammation as if it were a subject of rigid philosophy, carefully and patiently, and with the purpose of understanding every stage and step of it as you go along.

But there is no such thing as inflammation in the abstract. It must belong to some part or structure.

A man may practice physic without pathology, but he cannot be a first-rate practitioner without it.

There was one thing which I was not slow in finding out from morbid anatomy, viz. the great imperfection of the diagnostic part of medicine.

I confess (and it is my duty to confess) that the experience of after years, and the best care and watchfulness I could bestow upon individual cases, did not exempt me, in my turn, from the occasional mortification of finding upon dissection that a patient had died of an acute pleurisy, or an acute pericarditis, which I had never suspected during life; of pleurisy, however, much oftener than pericarditis.

Physicians do well to follow in the track of the pathologist. Our treatment of disease should strive to keep pace, if it can, with our knowledge of disease: but we must not be disappointed when it cannot.

There is no part of pathology which calls for the more earnest regard of medical men than the diseases of the endocardium, especially with a view of making out what they are, in their first formation, and noting, with clear marks of distinction, those which are simply inflammatory, and come within the possibility and promise of cure.

The disease, as traced out by dissection, was far from affording an entire explanation of the disease, as manifested by symptoms during life.

So far as morbid anatomy contemplates disease in progress, and scrutinizes and explains its organic processes, its value is very great.

It is among the general truths of pathology that parts left un-

87

sound by past disease have a greater readiness to catch disease afresh, from causes calculated to convey it, than parts which never were injured before. As a taper just blown out, will snatch the flame from the torch that scarcely touches it, and so rekindle itself at once.

The subjects of our profession require to be treated summarily or in detail, according to the degree of light that is brought to bear upon them from a general pathological principle. If you enter a spacious room with a small taper, you must carry it about, and pick your way with it into corners and recesses, round pillars and projections, and after all you will hardly know where you are, and will be lucky if you escape accidents. But if you enter the same with a bright burning lamp, you have only to place it on a pedestal, and then stand in the midst and look around; and then you will find all things, great and small, near and remote, brought out equally to view, and will at once understand and admire the beauty and proportions of the whole apartment.

Believe me, he who would be a first-rate practitioner must lay his foundations broad and deep in the knowledge of morbid processes; otherwise, although he may sometimes prognosticate truly concerning life and death he can never give an accurate diagnosis concerning the nature of diseases of which he can understand nothing. Above all, he must never hope to benefit mankind by advancing the knowledge of his profession a single step.

CHEMISTRY —
THE INTERNAL ATMOSPHERE

As there is an atmosphere without the man by which and in which whoever lives does live; so there is, what may be called, by just analogy, an atmosphere within the man by which and in which whoever lives does live.

The internal atmosphere (so-called from analogy) exists diffusively within us, and feeds our life.

Sagacious observers and experimenters have, in these later days, gone nigh to show that there is a chemistry within us which is cooperative with life; that making good its work, it gives to our bodies the materials of their health; and that doing its work faultily, it suffers noxious things to form, which become the elements of their diseases.

Let no man who is making his entrance into the medical profession henceforth ever neglect chemistry. Chemistry was once thought to be conversant only with the physiology of external nature; but every day is bringing us to look more and more to chemistry to explain the physiology of our own bodies.

PHYSIOLOGY

A great deal of what is termed physiology has turned out to be a mistake; and so far as it has got mixed up with our notions of disease (and this has happened to a deplorable extent), it has hindered the progress of practical medicine.

As the anatomy of healthy structure must always be the beginning and foundation of morbid anatomy, so must the physiology of healthy function be always the beginning and foundation of morbid physiology; for by this name of morbid physiology I will venture to call the knowledge of all the various ways in which the functions of the living body and its several parts are capable of being perverted and deranged.

That new method, in the course of time, was introduced, and is now popularly employed; it consists of research into morbid function and morbid structure, and is based upon the knowledge of healthy function and healthy structure. It is pathology founded upon physiology.

CLINICAL RESEARCH

People in general have no notion of the sort and amount of evidence often needed to prove the simplest matter of fact.

Clinical observation, with a view of keeping a man up to what is known, and perfecting him in its accustomed uses, may be an affair of sober industry only, of patient and almost passive looking on. But clinical observation, with a view of knowing more than is known, and turning new knowledge to its uses, belongs to an industry of another kind, to an energy ever active and stirring, and drawing upon, and working with the highest faculties of the mind.

The philosophical physician is evermore studying how, upon adequate grounds, he can assign to medical facts this relation. But he knows in how delicate and difficult a task he is engaged. He is obliged to wait upon experience, and to attend to phenomena as they happen to occur. He cannot bring them together at will, and vary and transpose them as he likes, so as to learn their connection. He envies the ease with which the chemist can bring any substance within the sphere and influence of as many others as he pleases; and the accuracy with which he can then ascertain the degrees of affinity it bears severally to each, — an accuracy so precise, that he can express them by numbers.

In medical science, the only materials of our knowledge are those things which are referable to our sensations and perceptions: matters of fact.

We always must form a judgment of what nature is aiming at whenever we interfere with what nature is doing.

EXPERIMENT

Experiment is like a man traveling to some far off place, and finding no place by the way where he can sit down and rest himself, and few or no guide posts to tell him whether he be in the right direction for it or not. Still he holds on. Perhaps he has been there before, and is pretty sure of this being the direction in which he found it. Or, perhaps he has never been there, but some of his friends have, and they told him of this being the right road to it. And so it may be that, by his own sagacity and the help of well-informed friends, he reaches it at last. Or, after all his own pains, and all his friends can do for him, it may be that he never reaches it at all.

Only consider what a vast number of comparative trials is needed to prove that one remedy has greater power than another to mitigate or arrest even actually existing symptoms; and then think of the infinitely greater number of such trials required to show one remedy more efficacious than another in preventing certain symptoms, which possibly might have been, but which never actually appeared.

The end of all the thought and labour of physicians is to make experiments with men's lives.

Questions of practical medicine are not to be settled like points of casuistry. The logical inference from the result of certain cases may incline one way, and the general mass of experience may incline another.

It has been reckoned among the triumphs of science to win a

new element from the jealousy and concealment of nature.

It is expedient that medical practice should in every case be conformed to the current idea of an experiment as far as the nature of that case will admit. No experience worthy of the name can be drawn from any number of cases less accurately followed up than they might have been.

The highest praise which the world has to bestow upon the physician is that he is experienced. There must, therefore, be a good deal worth knowing about this experience, which is deemed his characteristic excellence; as, how he goes to work in search of it, and how he gains it, experimenting after his manner, and with whatever help of science he can muster, or with none at all; but still experimenting.

The practice of medicine, when it is engaged in treating disease, acute disease especially, comes pretty near the current idea of experiment.

There is test and trial made of things one by one, and note taken of single consequences and effects as they arise under our hands, promising, promoting, and ending in the ultimate effect, which is the departure of disease and restoration to health.

I have myself a reasonable amount of faith in the power of medicine over chronic diseases. I have laid up a certain sum of experience fairly collected (as I believe) from experiments which I have been making all my life. But, then, all my life, I have been careful about my experiments, in this respect especially, I have sought to manage my cases of chronic diseases — in other words, to work my experiments — as much as possible by single remedies. On any other terms, I do not see how it were possible that I should have any faith at all.

When the one ultimate effect is near at hand, and follows rapidly upon the use of the remedy, as does the cure of ague upon the use of quinine, there is nothing wanting to the idea of an experiment in the completest practical sense.

In medical practice, as the one ultimate effect is more and more distant in point of time, and little or nothing is to be seen, or contrived, or done preparatorily and intermediately, the current idea of an experiment becomes obscured or well-nigh lost.

To those who walk about with their eyes open, objects often present themselves with a fidelity and truth which are too apt to suffer diminution and loss when the same objects are submitted to more curious experiments.

Chemical experiment and clinical observation, leading each other by the hand, proceed together, and arrive at the seminal principal of the disease.

EXPERIENCE

What with inscrutable things within the body and inscrutable things without, and incalculable and incontrollable withal, it is no wonder that Experience should sometimes find itself at fault, and be not always able to shape the future out of the past upon a large scale.

Wherefore then serveth *experience,* and of what use is it? Its first and best use is for the guidance of him that has it. Its next, and hardly less important use, is that it enables him to judge rightly the experience of others.

We physicians had need be a self-confronting and a self-reproving race; for we must be ready, without fear or favour, to call in question our own Experience and to judge it justly; to confirm it, to repeal it, to reverse it, to set up the new against the old, and again to reinstate the old and give it preponderance over the new.

The physician's success in the treatment of each particular case depends not upon the exact definition under which he can bring it, or the exact rule he can bring to bear upon it; but it comes from his own free choice of what is now best to be done, guided by the sum of all his former experience.

The progress of the human mind is evermore from particulars to generals; and he that would inform others must be careful, in the manner of his teaching, not to transgress the order of nature. Full of this important truth, I must first seek to rivet you to the contemplation of individuals, and only venture to unfold to you any general principles, which I may conceive myself to have reached, either of pathology or practice, in proportion as I judge you able to authenticate them by your own growing experience.

Nothing is so difficult to deal with as man's own Experience, how to value it according to its amount, what to conclude from it, and how to use it and do good with it.

How is it that Experience, upon which alone we can depend for all the good we do, is continually breaking down under us as a system?

Now it takes experience of a vast number of cases to make a man wise enough to pronounce confidently upon the issue of any form of disease. And experience is a thing which we must wait for; we cannot make it for ourselves.

I do not wish to exaggerate the difficulties of medical practice; neither do I wish to conceal them. I am sure you will never surmount them, unless you first feel and acknowledge them. And some practical experience is needed even for this.

94

The having to do with disease and remedies for thirty or forty years does of necessity no more make men experienced physicians, than looking upon the heavens all their lives makes them astronomers, or digging and delving the earth makes them geologists.

This power belongs to practical *experience* — to busy, thoughtful, multifarious experience—the honest and just judge that ultimately settles the worth of everything for physicians.

Truly do I wish that I could live a few past years again, and carry back with me my present experience for the sake of treating again some cases of rheumatic endocarditis, and of treating them better.

I cannot carry my experience backward, but you may carry it forward. And it is in the hope of some practical good to come from it, that I have thus analyzed and exposed it.

WORLDLY WISDOM

TALK AND PRAISE
Men are apt to talk largely and at random about what they are agreed to praise.

GOSSIP
It is easy to talk disparagingly of the best things.

ABOUT THINKING
Sure and great results — yet familiar and common, and procured at will and by certain means, but in an unaccountable manner — naturally set us thinking and forming notions how they come to pass . . .

SOUND JUDGEMENT
The mixture in this subject of equivocal facts and testimonies

95

with the true, needs, moreover, a pretty shrewd as well as a candid and wary mind to pick its way safely, a mind not over-credulous and seeing contagion in everything, yet not over sceptical and seeing it in nothing.

SOBER CONJECTURE

There is such a thing as sober conjecture, as well as sober certainty. And diseases are treated, and cures are achieved, and lives are saved, as often under the guidance of one as the other.

SYMPTOMS MAY NOT PARALLEL SEVERITY

It is a fallacy to conceive that disease, as represented by its symptoms, is difficult to know and to treat in proportion as it is a thing of more danger and severity.

WASTE

Superfluity of means leads to their useless expenditure.

("Parkinson's Law")

MOBS

Crowds keep one another in countenance where individuals feel sharply.

GRATITUDE

Benefits give pleasure as long as they seem within the possibility of repayment; when they have gone much beyond it, dislike takes the place of gratitude.

INSIGHT

Fortunate, indeed, is the man who takes exactly the right measure of himself, and holds a just balance between what he can acquire and what he can use, be it great or be it small!

EXAGGERATION

From controversy often comes exaggeration. And exaggeration often does the work of falsehood unawares.

BELIEFS FALSELY BASED

Men who have had great duties in hand, and who know *how*

they have done them, and feel that they have done them well, naturally hold strong practical beliefs; and these beliefs soon take the place of absolute truths in their minds.

SUBJECTIVITY

What an amazing difference there appears in the objects of nature around us, according to the point of view from which we regard them!

PRESCIENCE

But there is such a thing as having knowledge in reserve; such a thing as cherishing and increasing and perfecting it in hope, and looking patiently forward that the time may come when mankind shall be the better for it.

TASTE

There is much indifferent taste and worse judgment in the world, which are apt to applaud in the wrong place, and so to injure many things really good by their undiscerning patronage of them.

CLINICAL ICEBERGS

Look to the mere matter and bulk of things, and think only of what is visible, tangible and audible in parts, and you will come to strange conclusions: you will see people die of too little to kill them, and see people survive what is enough to kill them twenty times over.

ESSENCES

There are things which, as they ordinarily present themselves in nature, are so beset with collaterals that, but for their sometimes appearing in simple forms, they could never be fairly understood.

PERFECTION

Perfect health like perfect beauty, is a rare thing; and so, it seems, is perfect disease.

PROGRESS

It is unwise to treat of any medical subject as if it were complete.

CONFUSION

. . . practical medicine has from time to time been darkened, as it were, by cross lights, let in from strange quarters.

PRINCIPLES

Above all things we should covet principles; for most certainly they do not abound in practical medicine.

We must still concern ourselves with principles; we cannot help it; all men do it in some sort or other; for the mind is not able constantly to keep in view all the particulars of its own experience. It must needs reduce them within a narrower compass, and contemplate them (so to speak) in some representative.

IMPATIENCE

We should not be in a hurry to abandon such general facts as these which have often led us right, because they have sometimes seemed to lead us wrong.

DISCOVERY UPSETS OPINIONS

Whenever in medicine anything like a discovery has been made, anything which has had the show of a principle or a law, a large surrender of cherished opinions has always followed, and knowledge has seemeth to begin its career afresh from a new starting place.

HEARING GHOSTS

The knowledge of the senses is the best knowledge; but delusions of the senses are the worst delusions. And men are as often deceived by their ears as by their eyes; and they may hear ghosts as well as see them.

EXCEPTIONS

Individual experience, be it ever so large, is not all experience; and truths without exception are not the truths most commonly met within medicine.

THE UNKNOWN

There are things in our living bodies which have never yet been reached or touched by human knowledge. Much of health and disease, and life and death resides in these things; and the means and instruments of health and disease, and of life and death, are largely concerned with them.

SMALLNESS

It is hard to judge and decide truly upon our smaller perceptions; upon things which reach the sense, indeed, but strike them only feebly and faintly. Yet, when these smaller things have such important meanings as they have here, judge we must and decide we must, using all caution to avoid error.

DE MINIMIS

It requires some courage to talk gravely and with a purpose of instruction about common things. For either people do not listen at all, expecting to hear nothing new; or they listen reluctantly, not liking to be schooled about what they understand perfectly (they think) already.

CREDULITY

There is a credulity common enough among us; and this is in sympathy with the larger credulity of the world on medical subjects, and is strengthened by it. It incapacitates for all patient inquiry; and it may come to believe in everything.

TIME KEEPS SCHOOL

Time keeps school among physicians still. But he is not, and never was, a popular lecturer. He is slow in coming to the point. He has a cautious, hesitating, self-correcting manner, which is not altogether pleasant, and makes him difficult to follow.

THE DIFFICULTY OF MEDICAL FACTS

Now it must be confessed that there is no fact in medicine

(i.e. no fact respecting the animal body, its actions upon itself, or its obedience to other influences) which has the same character of universality with certain facts respecting the external world. In medicine we have no fact so universal as that all bodies unsupported fall to the ground, no principle so sure or irrefrangible as gravitation.

BEWARE OF PREMATURE SYSTEMATIZING

The great and frequent fault of our profession is to be premature and precipitate in systematizing new knowledge.

UNCOMMON SENSE

Common sense is in medicine the master workman.

Common sense may be sophisticated into folly, or it may be cultivated into sagacity, which is its highest perfection.

BEWARE AUTHORITIES

Beware of great authorities. They have a tyrannous way with them. They make common sense afraid to stand up and say what it knows to be right.

THE RARITY OF TRUE EXCELLENCE

My experience of human life has long since convinced me, that the number of truly learned and scientific men in the world is small.

WRONG THEORIES

It may be doubted whether the theories of clever men have not done more harm to the practice of medicine than all the mere blunders of the ignorant put together.

DETAILS

Nothing so vitiates the practice of medicine as that over-refinement, which either pretends to see more than be seen, or fritters away what it does see into endless idle particulars.

DISEASES ARE NOT ABSTRACTIONS

Every man's notion concerning any department of knowledge is the popular notion, until it is rectified by further inquiry. The popular notion concerning medicine is, that diseases are separate essences, and that an idea can be formed of them apart from the living being in whom they occur . . .

INCURABLE DISEASE

Many diseases which we knew the best, we did not therefore manage the better; often, indeed, not better than in the time of our ignorance; because a fatal part of our knowledge was simply this, that the diseases, in their own nature, were beyond the possible reach of any remedy.

EXCRETION

Of all organs of the body, those are most within the reach of medicine whose function is to secrete, and the products of whose secretion consist largely of refuse matter to be cast out of the system.

OPTIMISM

We should always presume the disease to be curable until its own nature prove it otherwise.

There is hardly a man living, be his disease what it may, who will bear to believe himself beyond the possibility of restoration to health.

. . . all mankind, in short, except physicians, even this entire world conceives all diseases that have a name as distinct essences, and of all remedies as distinct antidotes.

Oftentimes, in particular cases, we catch ourselves at work fabricating a sort of fictitious faith, and setting it up against all the experience of our lives, sooner than give the disease up for incurable.

I told them, however, what I knew of such cases, and made my little experience go as far as it would in the way of encouragement.

DUTY

The duty of physician to a great hospital, unless it can be made easy by indifference to its highest obligations, is incompatible with much care of personal health.

SKETCHES

Dr. Stevens, by experiment as a chemist, found that there was a condition of the blood in which it lost its due proportion of water, and its due proportion of neutral salts, especially common salt. And Dr. Stevens, by observation as a physician, learned that this condition of the blood was associated with the malignant symptoms of yellow fever. The contemplation of these facts led his mind to the employment of a new practice, the object of which was to give back its defective ingredients to the blood by the administration of salt and water; and thus he succeeded in curing an enormous proportion of those who, by any other method of treatment previously known, would have been thought incurable.

The great Lord Chatham, it is said, had such power of inspiring self-complacency into the minds of other men, that no one was ever a quarter of an hour in his company without believing that Lord Chatham was the first man in the world, and himself the second . . .

LIFE

Life is only known as the complex of many functions, and health as the integrity of these functions, each in itself, and their harmony among others.

It is often only when the powers of medicine are pressed even to the verge of destroying life, that life is saved.

DYING

The way of death is often smoother than the path of life; and great bodily anguish (there is reason to believe) does not often enter largely into the process of dissolution.

102

COLOPHON ❉ This book has been designed and printed by Carroll Coleman at The Prairie Press in Iowa City, Iowa